A TEXT-BOC

CONVERG

A TEXT-BOOK OF
CONVERGENCE

BY

W. L. FERRAR

M.A., D.Sc.

OXFORD

AT THE CLARENDON PRESS

Oxford University Press, Walton Street, Oxford OX2 6DP

OXFORD LONDON GLASGOW
NEW YORK TORONTO MELBOURNE WELLINGTON
KUALA LUMPUR SINGAPORE HONG KONG TOKYO
DELHI BOMBAY CALCUTTA MADRAS KARACHI
NAIROBI DAR ES SALAAM CAPE TOWN

First published 1938
Reprinted from corrected sheets of the First Edition
1945, 1947, 1951, 1956, 1959, 1963, 1969
New as Paperback 1980

British Library Cataloguing in Publication Data
Ferrar, William Leonard
 A text-book of convergence
 1. Sequences (Mathematics)
 2. Series
 3. Convergence
 I. Title
 515'.24   QA292   79–41369
 ISBN 0–19–853176–1

*Printed in Great Britain
at the University Press, Oxford
by Eric Buckley
Printer to the University*

PREFACE

THIS book is written primarily for undergraduates, though Part I may be judged by some teachers to be suitable for mathematicians during their last year at school. It includes the convergence theory that is commonly required for a university honours course in pure and applied mathematics, but excludes topics appropriate to post-graduate or to highly specialized courses of study. It has taken shape from sets of lectures I have given at various times during some fifteen years of university teaching.

The book develops the theory of convergence on the basis of two fundamental assumptions (one about upper bounds, one about irrational number as the limit of a sequence of rational numbers). With these assumptions the theory of convergence can be developed without appeal to the properties of Dedekind cuts. The 'real number' appears in the appendix, where the assumptions of the book are proved to be consequences of the definition of 'real number'.

The notation, or shorthand, used in the text is one that is familiar to the professed analyst and is a commonplace of the lecture-room. It is something of an experiment to employ it in a text-book, but its almost universal adoption in recent years by mathematical undergraduates at Oxford leads me to hope that it will prove acceptable. My own teaching experience is that students who use the notation acquire clear ideas of what they have to prove and of how they may prove it.

Of the details, few call for mention in the preface. The treatment of Tannery's theorem in Chapter XVI grew out of (i) Professor E. H. Neville's note in the *Mathematical Gazette*, vol. xv, p. 166, (ii) a remark once made to me by Professor Hardy, and (iii) my own work on a special series. I cannot resolve how much is due to each, but I am sure the chapter owes much both to Professor Neville and to Professor Hardy, and I gladly take this opportunity of acknowledging my indebtedness to them. The brief chapter on Fourier series will, I hope, prove useful in spite of its brevity and many omissions. The appendix contains just so much of the 'foundations of analysis' as is necessary to the justification of the assumptions made in the early chapters of the book. These 'foundations' are prefaced by a very brief historical sketch that tries to show why such a complex structure as a Dedekind cut is necessary to the definition of 'number'.

All theorems are numbered. Some references to previous theorems are given in parentheses; if the reader can follow the proofs without consulting these references, so much the better. They are given so that readers may, if necessary, look up points they have forgotten: it is not intended that proofs in convergence theory should bristle with references to previous theorems in the manner of the old Euclid books. Though, of course, the order of proof is as important here as it is in the development of Euclidean geometry: we must not use A to prove B, and then use B to prove A.

The examples contain many questions set in university examinations and many questions taken from my own notes; of the latter, some are original and some are not. The majority are reasonably straightforward; hints for their solution are occasionally given. There are a few examples marked '*Harder*', and the beginner is advised not to attempt them on a first reading.

Professor A. L. Dixon and Professor E. T. Copson have kindly read the proof sheets, and I am deeply grateful to them both for their helpful criticisms. Professor Copson has read and criticized all the text and has worked nearly all the examples. I wish to thank him most sincerely for this evidence of his friendship.

In conclusion, I should like to thank the staff of the Oxford University Press for their work on the book and for their unfailing courtesy towards me in all matters concerning it.

W.L.F

HERTFORD COLLEGE,
OXFORD
16 *November* 1937.

CONTENTS

PART I

A FIRST COURSE IN THE THEORY OF SEQUENCES AND SERIES

CHAPTER I
PRELIMINARY DISCUSSION

1. Definition. A set of numbers in a definite order of occurrence,
$$\alpha_1,\ \alpha_2,\ \alpha_3,...,\ \alpha_n,...,$$
is called a SEQUENCE.

EXAMPLES. $5,\ 6,\ 7;\quad \dfrac{1}{2},\ \dfrac{1}{4},\ \dfrac{1}{8},...,\ \dfrac{1}{2^n},...;\quad \dfrac{1}{3},\ -\dfrac{1}{5},\ \dfrac{1}{7},\ -\dfrac{1}{9},....$

If the sequence stops, as in the first example, which has only three terms, it is called a FINITE SEQUENCE. If the sequence does not stop, as in the second and third examples, it is called an INFINITE SEQUENCE.

In what follows we shall be concerned chiefly with infinite sequences. We shall use three notations for a sequence:

$$\alpha_1,\ \alpha_2,\ \alpha_3,...,\ \alpha_n,...,$$
$$\alpha_n \quad (n = 1, 2,...),$$
or simply $\qquad (\alpha_n).$

The advantages of alternative notations soon become apparent.

2. Preliminary discussion of convergence

2.1. Throughout the rest of this chapter we shall discuss, with no attempt at final precision, some of the ideas which are the subject of the more precise work in Chapter II. We begin with an elementary example of an infinite series, namely
$$1+\tfrac{1}{2}+\tfrac{1}{4}+\tfrac{1}{8}+.... \tag{1}$$
If s_n is the sum of the first n terms of this series, then
$$s_n = 2\left(1-\frac{1}{2^n}\right) = 2-(\tfrac{1}{2})^{n-1}.$$

As n grows large, $(\tfrac{1}{2})^{n-1}$ becomes small, and, in fact, we can make $(\tfrac{1}{2})^{n-1}$ as small as we please by taking n large enough. In other words, s_n approximates to 2 as n becomes large. We say, accordingly, that s_n converges to (i.e. approaches or approximates to) 2. THIS IS THE GENERAL NOTION UNDERLYING CONVERGENCE— CONVERGENCE IS 'APPROACHING', OR 'APPROXIMATION'.

Suppose we are given any infinite series

$$u_1 + u_2 + u_3 + \dots. \tag{2}$$

Let $s_n \equiv u_1 + u_2 + \dots + u_n$. We say that the series (2) converges if s_n, as n becomes large, approaches some definite number s. THIS NUMBER s IS CALLED THE SUM OF THE SERIES; the series itself is said to converge, or to be convergent.

Notice that this use of the word 'sum' is not the same as its use when we say that 'the sum of $1 + \frac{1}{2} + \frac{1}{4}$ is $1\frac{3}{4}$'. It is a special use of the word 'sum' in its application to infinite series.

An example of a convergent series.

$$\frac{1}{1.2.3} + \frac{1}{2.3.4} + \dots + \frac{1}{n(n+1)(n+2)} + \dots \tag{3}$$

Here, the nth term, u_n, is given by

$$u_n = \frac{1}{n(n+1)(n+2)} = \frac{1}{2}\left\{\frac{1}{n(n+1)} - \frac{1}{(n+1)(n+2)}\right\},$$

and so $\quad u_1 + u_2 + \dots + u_n = \frac{1}{2}\left\{\frac{1}{1.2} - \frac{1}{(n+1)(n+2)}\right\}.$

Accordingly, $\quad s_n \equiv u_1 + u_2 + \dots + u_n$

approaches $\frac{1}{4}$ as n becomes large: we say that the series (3) converges and that its sum is $\frac{1}{4}$.

NOTE. This is a standard method of dealing with a standard type of series, namely the type in which the nth term, u_n, can be expressed in the form $v_n - v_{n+1}$.

EXAMPLES I

1. If $u_n = \dfrac{1}{n(n+1)(n+2)(n+3)}$, then $u_1 + u_2 + \dots$ is a convergent series and its sum is $1/18$.

2. If $u_n = \dfrac{1}{n(n+2)}$, then

$$u_1 + u_2 + \dots + u_n = \frac{1}{2}\left(\frac{3}{2} - \frac{1}{n+1} - \frac{1}{n+2}\right),$$

$u_1 + u_2 + \dots$ is a convergent series, and its sum is $\frac{3}{4}$.

3. If $u_n = \dfrac{n}{(n+1)(n+2)(n+3)}$, show, by using partial fractions, that

$$u_1 + u_2 + \ldots + u_n = \frac{1}{4} + \frac{1}{2}\left(\frac{1}{n+2} - \frac{3}{n+3}\right).$$

Hence show that $u_1 + u_2 + \ldots$ is convergent, and its sum is $\frac{1}{4}$.

4. Find the sum of the series $u_1 + u_2 + u_3 + \ldots$ when u_n is

   (i) $\dfrac{2n+3}{(n+1)(n+2)(n+3)}$,   (ii) $\dfrac{n^2}{(n-1)n(n+1)(n+2)}$,

   (iii) $\dfrac{2n+1}{n^2(n+1)^2}$,   (iv) $\dfrac{3n+5}{(n+1)(n+2)(n+3)}$.

2.2. Series which diverge. Consider the series

$$1+2+3+\ldots+n+\ldots. \tag{4}$$

Here $s_n = u_1 + u_2 + \ldots + u_n = 1 + 2 + \ldots + n$
$$= \tfrac{1}{2}n(n+1).$$

In this example, if n is large, then so is s_n.

For our purposes we need some refinement of the last statement. In discussing the series (1) we stressed the fact that 'we can make the difference between s_n and 2 as small as we please'. Here, with series (4), we can make s_n as large as we please by taking n sufficiently large. The refinement we fasten on, then, is this: *The sequence s_n increases indefinitely; that is to say, whatever positive number A we care to put down, s_n will exceed A if we choose n large enough.*

The series (4) is said to diverge, or to be divergent.

Another example of a divergent series is

$$1 + 2 + 2^2 + \ldots + 2^{n-1} + \ldots. \tag{5}$$

Here $s_n = 1 + 2 + \ldots + 2^{n-1} = 2^n - 1$, and again s_n increases indefinitely.

2.3. The dependence of series on sequences. In the

foregoing discussion of the convergence or divergence of a given series,

$$u_1 + u_2 + \ldots + u_n + \ldots,$$

we have seen that it is the behaviour of the sequence

$$s_1, s_2, \ldots, s_n, \ldots,$$

where $s_n \equiv u_1 + u_2 + \ldots + u_n$, which is in question.

We shall, accordingly, leave aside infinite series for a while and turn our attention to sequences.

3. Sequences that converge to zero

(i) *If* $0 < x < 1$, *then the sequence*

$$x, x^2, x^3, ..., x^n, ...$$

converges to zero.

To see this, put $y = (1/x)$, so that $y > 1$. Put

$$y = 1+p \quad (p > 0).$$

Then $\qquad y^2 = 1+2p+p^2 > 1+2p,$

and, by induction, $\qquad y^n > 1+np.$

Accordingly, y^n increases indefinitely and x^n, or y^{-n}, decreases indefinitely in the sense that we can make its value as near nothing as we please by taking n large enough.

(ii) This example is much more difficult: its result is often useful. [It may be omitted on the first reading.]

If y *is a fixed number greater than unity, and* k *is any fixed positive integer, then the sequence*

$$n^k/y^n \quad (n = 1, 2, ...)$$

converges to zero.

Before we give the proof of this theorem we try to explain some of the ideas that lead to the proof.

(i) Numbers like $10^6 - 5$, $10^6 + 7$ are 'about as big' as 10^6: in calculations involving numbers as big as 10^6, a relatively small number like 5 or 7, when added to or subtracted from 10^6, will have very little effect on the result of the calculations.

If l is a fixed number and n is to be thought of as a very large number, then $n-l$ is 'about as big' as n. Further, extending this idea a little, if k is a fixed number and n is to be thought of as a very large number, then

$$n(n-1)(n-2)...(n-k)$$

is 'about as big' as n^{k+1}.

This idea is useful in many problems.

(ii) The y of our problem exceeds unity and we can write

$$y^n = (1+p)^n \quad (p > 0).$$

The right-hand side can be expanded, when n is a positive integer, by the binomial theorem, and, since each term of the expansion is positive, the whole is greater than any single term of the expansion.

So, if we take $n > k+1$,

$$y^n = (1+p)^n > \frac{n(n-1)...(n-k)}{(k+1)!} p^{k+1}.$$

(iii) Hence, when n is thought of as a large number,

$$n^k/y^n$$

is n^k divided by a number about as big as (or bigger than)

$$n^{k+1}p^{k+1}/(k+1)!$$

Now p and k are fixed, and so n^k/y^n is, for large n, comparable with a fixed multiple of $(1/n)$, and we can make its value as near zero as we please by choosing n large enough.

Formal proof. We are concerned with what happens when n is large; so we may confine our attention to values of n that exceed $k+1$. When $n > k+1$ and $y = 1+p$, where $p > 0$,

$$y^n = (1+p)^n > \frac{n(n-1)\ldots(n-k)}{(k+1)!}p^{k+1}$$

$$> (n-k)^{k+1}p^{k+1}/(k+1)!$$

Hence $\qquad \dfrac{n^k}{y^n} < \dfrac{(k+1)!}{p^{k+1}} \dfrac{n^k}{n^{k+1}(1-k/n)^{k+1}}.$

[This step arrives at the n^k/n^{k+1} which our preliminary talk led us to expect—we now get rid of n from all other terms.]

But, when $n > k+1$,

$$1-\frac{k}{n} > 1-\frac{k}{k+1} = \frac{1}{k+1},$$

and so $\qquad \dfrac{n^k}{y^n} < \dfrac{(k+1)!\,(k+1)^{k+1}}{p^{k+1}}\cdot\dfrac{1}{n},$

and the theorem follows [p, k are *fixed* numbers].

NOTE. Having isolated the n^{k+1} of y^n, we use the roughest of inequalities to deal with the rest: the sole object of the manipulations is to remove n from every place save the one essential place where we want it at the end, namely $1/n$.

CHAPTER II

FORMAL DEFINITIONS

1. Formal definitions of convergence

1.1. Sequences which converge to zero.

A sequence like

$$\alpha_n = (-)^n n^{-1} \quad (n = 1, 2, ...)$$

shows that the approach to zero need not be from one side only. It is the absolute value† of α_n, that is, in the usual notation, $|\alpha_n|$, which is in question.

A sequence like

$$\frac{1}{2}, 1, \frac{1}{4}, \frac{1}{3}, ..., \frac{1}{2n}, \frac{1}{2n-1}, ...,$$

though artificial in structure, is enough to show that a sequence α_n can approach zero without having its terms become steadily smaller: the approach to zero need not be a steady one.

Finally, one is tempted to say that α_n will converge to zero if α_n can be made as small as we please 'by taking n sufficiently large'. But this is not quite accurate. In the sequence

$$\frac{1}{2}, \frac{1}{3}, 1, \frac{1}{4}, \frac{1}{5}, 2, ..., \frac{1}{2k}, \frac{1}{2k+1}, k, ... \tag{A}$$

we can make the nth term as small as we please by taking n sufficiently large if we keep to values of n that are not multiples of 3. The sequence as a whole does not converge to zero because, in every third place, the sequence $1, 2, 3, ...$ runs through it. In our formal definition we use the phrase 'by taking any n that is sufficiently large' instead of 'by taking n sufficiently large'. We cannot make the nth term of (A) as small as we please by taking *any* n that is sufficiently large; we can do so only by taking *certain* n that are sufficiently large.

These preliminary remarks made, we give our first form of the definition.

DEFINITION. FORM A. The sequence

$$\alpha_1, \alpha_2, ..., \alpha_n, ...$$

is said to converge, or tend, to zero (in symbols, $\alpha_n \to 0$)

† If α is a real number, $|\alpha| = \alpha$ when α is positive and $|\alpha| = -\alpha$ when α is negative; e.g. $|-6| = 6$, $|7| = 7$.

'*if* $|\alpha_n|$ *can be made as small as we please by taking any* n *that is sufficiently large*'.

Let us examine this and put it wholly into symbols. We 'can make $|\alpha_n|$ as small as we please' if, on putting down any positive number ϵ whatsoever, we can make $|\alpha_n| < \epsilon$. 'By taking any n that is sufficiently large' means that the relation in question, namely $|\alpha_n| < \epsilon$, will hold for all values of $n \geqslant$ some definite number, N say.

Hence, our condition that $\alpha_n \to 0$ may be stated in the form B, given below.

FORM B. $\alpha_n \to 0$ *if, having chosen any positive number* ϵ *whatsoever, we can then find a definite number* N *such that*

$$|\alpha_n| < \epsilon \quad when \ n \geqslant N.$$

The important point to notice is that, for α_n to tend to zero, we must be able to find our N no matter what positive ϵ we have chosen to start with: it is not enough to be able to find N when we have taken ϵ to be one particular very small number like 10^{-6}. We have to be able to make $|\alpha_n|$ *as small as we please* and not merely as small as 10^{-6}.

1.2. The definition in symbols. We now introduce a notation that is useful both in curtailing long-winded statements and in helping one to handle the technique of convergence questions.

We write down form B in this notation: it becomes

FORM C. $\alpha_n \to 0$ *if*

$$\epsilon > 0; \quad \exists \ N \ . \ |\alpha_n| < \epsilon \quad when \ n \geqslant N.$$

In reading this notation, what comes *before* the semicolon is set down to begin with (and is subject to no limitation that is not explicitly shown), what comes *after* the semicolon is dependent on what comes before. In detail the notation is read

(i) $\epsilon > 0$; 'on putting down any positive number ϵ whatsoever to begin with',

(ii) ; separates what is put down to begin with from what can be said after it has been put down,

(iii) ∃ means 'there exists', 'there is (a number)',

(iv) the point . means 'such that'. [It is useful to have a shorthand for this frequently used phrase.]

Thus the whole reads '$\alpha_n \to 0$ if, on putting down any positive number ϵ whatsoever to begin with, there is some number N such that $|\alpha_n| < \epsilon$ when $n \geqslant N$'.

1.3. The three definitions. The form A says all that is necessary but, in the technique of later work, it is not so convenient as the form B, and this again is not so convenient as the form C. All three say the same thing in a different form of words.

In using C it must always be remembered that $\epsilon > 0$; means 'putting down any positive number ϵ *whatsoever* TO BEGIN WITH'. The ϵ is set down at the beginning, a fact that cannot be stressed too much.

2. Sequences that converge, but not to zero

2.1. FORM A. *The sequence* $\alpha_1, \alpha_2, ..., \alpha_n, ...$ *is said to converge or tend to* l *(in symbols,* $\alpha_n \to l$*) if the sequence*

$$\alpha_1 - l, \ \alpha_2 - l, ..., \ \alpha_n - l, ...$$

tends to zero.

If we use the forms B and C of the definition in § 1, this becomes

FORM B. $\alpha_n \to l$ *if, having chosen any positive number* ϵ *whatsoever, we can then find a definite number* N *such that*

$$|\alpha_n - l| < \epsilon \quad when \ n \geqslant N.$$

FORM C. $\alpha_n \to l$, *if*

$$\epsilon > 0; \ \exists \ N \ . \ |\alpha_n - l| < \epsilon \quad when \ n \geqslant N.$$

The form C is, of course, the shorthand or symbolic form of B.

2.2. NOTATION. We call l, above, the 'limit' of the sequence (α_n).

3. Properties of convergent sequences

3.1. THEOREM 1. *A convergent sequence is bounded, i.e. if* $\alpha_n \to \alpha$, *then there is a number* K *such that*

$$|\alpha_n| < K \quad for \ \text{ALL} \ n.$$

We shall use, here and later, the shorthand (or notation) of § 1.2.

Proof. Since $\alpha_n \to \alpha$,

$$\exists \; N_1 \; . \; |\alpha_n - \alpha| < 1 \quad when \; n \geqslant N_1. \tag{1}$$

[In the forms B and C of our definition, ϵ is any positive number whatsoever: in the line (1) we choose to take $\epsilon = 1$: we have a special object in view and any definite choice of an ϵ will serve our present, very special, purpose.]

Hence,† when $n \geqslant N_1$,

$$|\alpha_n| = |(\alpha_n - \alpha) + \alpha|$$
$$\leqslant |\alpha_n - \alpha| + |\alpha|$$
$$\leqslant 1 + |\alpha|. \tag{2}$$

The numbers $|\alpha_1|, |\alpha_2|, ..., |\alpha_{N_1-1}|$ form a finite set of numbers and so one of them, $|\alpha_r| = K_1$ say, is greater than or equal to each and every other one of the set.

$$\therefore \; |\alpha_n| \leqslant \text{a definite } K_1 \quad when \; n < N_1. \tag{3}$$

From (2) and (3), if K is any number greater than K_1 and $1 + |\alpha|$, then
$$|\alpha_n| < K \quad for \; all \; n.$$

3.2. THEOREM 2. *If $\alpha_n \to \alpha$ and $\alpha_n > c$ for all n, then we can deduce that $\alpha \geqslant c$. We* CANNOT, *from the hypotheses, deduce that $\alpha > c$.*

Proof. Let λ be any number less than c. Then $c - \lambda$ is a definite positive number and

$$\alpha_n - \lambda > c - \lambda > 0.$$

Hence $|\alpha_n - \lambda|$, which is $\alpha_n - \lambda$, is never less than a certain positive number $c - \lambda$ and so, as we see from form B of § 2, α_n cannot converge to λ.

That is, α_n cannot converge to any number less than c, and so $\alpha \geqslant c$.

---

† Note, for all work with absolute values,

$$|a+b| \leqslant |a| + |b|.$$

If the result is not known, it can easily be verified when a and b are real numbers.

An example to show that α may be equal to c.
Let $\alpha_n = n^{-1}$, so that $\alpha_n \to 0$, i.e. $\alpha = 0$. Here, for each value of n, $\alpha_n > 0$, but $\alpha = 0$.

COROLLARY. *If $\alpha_n \to \alpha$ and $\alpha_n < c$ for all n, then we can deduce that $\alpha \leqslant c$.*

4. Formal definitions of divergence

4.1. Sequences which diverge through positive values.

We give three forms of the definition of a divergent sequence; each says the same thing in a different way. The three forms A, B, C correspond to the three forms used for convergent sequences in §§ 1, 2.

DEFINITION. *The sequence*
$$\alpha_1, \alpha_2, \ldots, \alpha_n, \ldots$$
is said to diverge through positive values

FORM A. *if α_n increases indefinitely.*

FORM B. *if, having chosen any positive number A whatsoever, we can then find a definite number N such that $\alpha_n > A$ when $n \geqslant N$.*

FORM C. $A > 0$; $\exists\, N$. $\alpha_n > A$ *when $n \geqslant N$.*

EXAMPLES. (i) $\alpha_n = n$. Whatever positive number A we set down, $\alpha_n > A$ if $n \geqslant 1 + A$.
(ii) $\alpha_n = (1+p)^n$, where $p > 0$. We know (§ 3) that $\alpha_n > 1+np$, so that $\alpha_n > A$ when $1+np \geqslant A$, that is, when $n \geqslant (A-1)/p$.

4.2. Sequences which diverge through negative values.

The sequence
$$(\alpha_n), \quad \text{i.e. } \alpha_1, \alpha_2, \alpha_3, \ldots, \alpha_n, \ldots,$$
is said to diverge through negative values if the sequence
$$(-\alpha_n), \quad \text{i.e. } -\alpha_1, -\alpha_2, \ldots, -\alpha_n, \ldots,$$
diverges through positive values.

EXAMPLES. (i) $\alpha_n = -n$; (ii) $\alpha_n = -n^2$.

4.3. Non-convergent sequences.

There are certain sequences that are neither convergent nor divergent. An example is
$$1, 0, 1, 0, 1, 0, \ldots,$$
or again
$$1, \tfrac{1}{2}, 2, \tfrac{1}{3}, 3, \tfrac{1}{4}, 4, \ldots.$$
We call such sequences 'non-convergent' or 'oscillating'.

5. Important properties of finite sequences

5.1. Least terms of sequences.

If we have a finite number of terms

$$a_1, a_2, ..., a_n,$$

n terms in all, then there must be one of them which is less than or equal to each and every other term. For example, in

$$1, 2, 3, 3, 2, 1,$$

six terms in all, the first is less than or equal to each of the others.

If we have an infinite sequence

$$a_1, a_2, a_3, ...,$$

there may or may not be such a term. For example:

(i) $1, 2, 3, ...$ is an infinite sequence and the first term is less than any other,

(ii) $1, \frac{1}{2}, \frac{1}{3}, ...$ is an infinite sequence and whatever term of it we take we can always find a term less than it.

We cannot speak of the least term (or terms) of an infinite sequence until we have shown that there is one.

This simple fact is one of the fundamental differences between a 'finite number of terms' and 'an infinity of terms'. The same remark applies, of course, to the 'greatest term'.

In the same order of ideas, if we have a finite sequence

$$a_1, a_2, ..., a_n,$$

n terms in all, then the sequence is necessarily bounded, that is, there is some number K such that $|a_r| < K$ for $r = 1, 2, ..., n$. With an infinite sequence this is not so, it may or may not be bounded. For example, a divergent sequence is not bounded, whereas (Theorem 1) a convergent sequence is bounded.

6. A practical way of looking at convergence

Suppose $\alpha_n \to l$. Then

$$\epsilon > 0; \quad \exists \ N \ . \ |\alpha_n - l| < \epsilon \quad \text{when } n \geqslant N. \tag{1}$$

Think of the point l and the various points α_n marked off on a straight line, using distances from a fixed point O. Then (1) says WHATEVER marks we make at a distance ϵ on each side of l, then, from and after *some* value N, α_n will lie within these marks. The value of N will depend, of course, on where we put the marks.

If we know that $\alpha_n \to l$, we can sometimes get all the facts we want for our subsequent work by making the marks in special places. Thus, suppose $l > 0$, as in Fig. A. We can

| O | $l-\epsilon$ | l | $l+\epsilon$ | | $2l$ | l | O |

FIG. A.   FIG. B.

put the marks at $\frac{1}{2}l$ and $\frac{3}{2}l$ and then, if $a_n \to l$, we can say that, when $n \geqslant$ some definite N, $\alpha_n > \frac{1}{2}l$. Again, if $l < 0$, as in Fig. B, we can put the marks at 0 and $2l$, and so there is a number N such that $\alpha_n < 0$ when $n \geqslant N$.

Readers will best see the force of these remarks when they come to Theorem 12, though they are useful in many other connexions.

EXAMPLES II

1. Prove that the sequence (α_n) converges to zero when α_n is given by

(i) $(-)^n \dfrac{1}{n}$,   (ii) $\dfrac{n+1}{n^2+2}$,   (iii) $\dfrac{1}{\sqrt{n}}$,   (iv) $\dfrac{n^2+3}{n^3-1}$,   (v) $\dfrac{n+5}{\sqrt{n^3}}$.

The point of such examples is to show that form B (or C) is satisfied. They are intended for practice only: a much more efficient method of proving the results will be given in Chap. VI, § 2.2.

In approaching an example, such as the fourth, it is simplest to work in this way.

First. We may expect $(n^2+3)/(n^3-1)$ to behave very much like n^2/n^3 when n is a large number.

[In a numerical calculation where $n = 10^6$, say, we would never concern ourselves with the difference between 10^{12} and $10^{12}+3$.]

Second. The actual work, which is guided by the thought contained in the first:

$$n^2+3 < 2n^2 \quad \text{when } n \geqslant 2,$$

$$n^3-1 > \tfrac{1}{2}n^3 \quad \text{when } n \geqslant 2.$$

Hence $0 < \alpha_n < 4n^{-1}$ when $n \geqslant 2$. Accordingly, $\epsilon > 0$; [or, in full, on putting down any positive number ϵ whatsoever]

$$|\alpha_n| < \epsilon \quad \text{when } n \geqslant 1/4\epsilon \text{ and } n \geqslant 2,$$

and so the condition that $\alpha_n \to 0$ is satisfied.

NOTE. Actually, one could prove that when n is large enough

$$\alpha_n < \frac{1}{n} + \frac{3 \cdot 1}{n^2} \quad \left[\text{or} \ \frac{3 \cdot 00 \ldots 1}{n^2} \right],$$

but there is no point here in doing anything more subtle than 'get the n^{-1} standing clear with *some* definite numerical multiplier', such as 4.

2. Prove that $\alpha_n \to 1, 3, 4$ according as α_n is given by

(i) $\dfrac{n}{n+1}$, (ii) $\dfrac{3n^2+1}{n^2-5n}$ $(n > 5)$, (iii) $\dfrac{4n^3+6n-7}{n^3-2n^2+1}$ $(n > 1)$.

We work (ii). We may expect the sequence to approach the same value as $3n^2/n^2$, i.e. 3 [for n^2 will outweigh n when n is large]. Now

$$3 - \frac{3n^2+1}{n^2-5n} = -\frac{15n+1}{n^2-5n},$$

and $n^2 - 5n > \frac{1}{2}n^2$ when $n > 10$. Hence, when $n > 10$,

$$\left| 3 - \frac{3n^2+1}{n^2-5n} \right| < \frac{16n}{\frac{1}{2}n^2} = \frac{32}{n},$$

and so $\quad \epsilon > 0; \quad \left| 3 - \dfrac{3n^2+1}{n^2-5n} \right| < \epsilon$ when $n \geqslant \dfrac{32}{\epsilon}$.

Hence $\quad \epsilon > 0; \quad \exists \ N \ . \ |\alpha_n - 3| < \epsilon$ when $n \geqslant N$.

3. Show that the sequence (α_n) given by (i) in Example 2 has a least but not a greatest member.

Harder. In Example 2 (iii), (α_n) has a greatest but not a least member. [Write α_n in the form $4 + (8n^2 + 6n - 11)/(n^3 - 2n^2 + 1)$.]

4. Show that the sequence (x^n) tends to zero when x is a fixed positive number less than unity.

5. Show that, when y is a fixed number that exceeds unity and k is a fixed positive integer, the sequence (n^k/y^n) converges to zero. [Cf. Chap. I, § 3, where, however, the formal definitions of convergence were not used.]

6. Prove that, if c is a constant and if $\alpha_n \to \alpha$, then $\alpha_n + c \to \alpha + c$ and $c\alpha_n \to c\alpha$.

7. Prove that, if $\alpha_n \to \alpha$, then $|\alpha_n| \to |\alpha|$.

8. Show that the sequence (α_n) diverges through negative values when α_n is given by

(i) $6 - n^2$, (ii) -2^n, (iii) $(-3)^{2n+1}$.

CHAPTER III

BOUNDS: MONOTONIC SEQUENCES

1. The bounds of a sequence

1.1. A fundamental assumption. In the next section,
1.2, we make an assumption; namely, that a certain set of numbers has in it a *least* number. The assumption is marked with an asterisk. If we are prepared to make a thorough examination of the definition and theory of real number, we can prove that the assumption is justified. This examination is made in the appendix (it is not altogether easy), and in the course of that examination our assumption appears as a theorem.

1.2. The upper bound of a sequence. Let (α_n) be any sequence of real numbers. Then

EITHER (i) there is a number $\geqslant$ every α_n, and so there is an infinity of such numbers,

OR (ii) there is not a number $\geqslant$ every α_n.

In case (i), having fixed on one such number, then every greater number is also $\geqslant$ every α_n, and possibly, though not certainly, there may be a less number with this property ($\geqslant$ every α_n).

ASSUMPTION 1.* *We assume that in case* (i) *there is a least number, U say, which is greater than or equal to each and every α_n.*

DEFINITION. *The* UPPER BOUND, *U, of a sequence* (α_n) *is the least number which is greater than or equal to each and every α_n.*

It follows at once from the definition that if U' is any number less than U, then there is at least one α_n that exceeds U'. We embody this important fact in the theorem which follows.

THEOREM 3. *If U is the upper bound of (α_n), then, given any number U' less than U, there is at least one α_n such that*

$$U' < \alpha_n \leqslant U.$$

In case (ii) the sequence (α_n) has no upper bound (in the sense of the previous definition). The definition that follows is an alternative way of stating the same fact.

DEFINITION. *If there is no number $\geqslant$ each and every α_n, we say that the* UPPER BOUND *of* (α_n) *is plus infinity* $[+\infty]$.

This is merely a convenient way of saying 'whatever number A we take, there is at least one α_n that exceeds A'. The definition does not postulate a number 'infinity'.

When we are dealing with case (i), and so with the definition on p. 16, we shall refer to the upper bound as finite.

The LOWER BOUND of a sequence is similarly defined: it may be finite or 'minus infinity'.

1.3. It is convenient at this point, having introduced one conventional use of the word 'infinity', to notice others of a like character.

If α_n diverges through positive (negative) values, then we say that α_n diverges, or tends, to plus (minus) infinity We write $\alpha_n \to +\infty, -\infty$, as the case may be.

If the sequence (α_n) converges to α (compare the definitions of Chap. II, §§ 1, 2), we sometimes, for convenience, say that α_n tends to α as n tends to infinity; in symbols, $\alpha_n \to \alpha$ as $n \to \infty$, or

$$\lim_{n \to \infty} \alpha_n = \alpha.$$

1.4. Examples of upper and lower bounds. In many examples it is easy enough to see what the upper and lower bounds are.

With the (infinite) sequence of numbers

$$1, \frac{1}{2}, \frac{1}{3}, \ldots, \frac{1}{n}, \ldots,$$

1 is clearly the least number that has the property of being greater than or equal to each and every number in the sequence; 0 the greatest number that has the property of being less than or equal to each and every number in the sequence. Hence, the upper bound is 1 and the lower bound is 0.

[Notice that it is 'greater than or equal to'. Assumption 1 would be completely false if it said merely 'greater than'. There cannot be a least number greater than 1: for suppose x to be the least number greater than 1; then $\frac{1}{2}x > \frac{1}{2}$ and $\frac{1}{2}(1+x) > 1$, while $\frac{1}{2}(1+x) < x$; and so x cannot be the least number greater than 1.]

Again, with the sequence

$$0, -1, -2, -3, ...,$$

0 is clearly the least number greater than or equal to each and every number of the sequence, and so the upper bound is 0; but the numbers decrease indefinitely and the lower bound is $-\infty$.

2. Monotonic sequences

2.1. DEFINITION. *When* $\alpha_{n+1} \geqslant \alpha_n$ *for all values of* n, *the sequence* (α_n) *is said to be* MONOTONIC INCREASING, *or, in abbreviated form,* m.i.

When $\alpha_{n+1} > \alpha_n$ for all values of n, the sequence is said to be steadily increasing or monotonic increasing in the strict sense. The difference lies in the exclusion of the possibility $\alpha_{n+1} = \alpha_n$ for some or all values of n: it is not often needed, but is occasionally important.

A MONOTONIC DECREASING (m.d.) sequence is similarly defined; (α_n) is m.d. if $\alpha_{n+1} \leqslant \alpha_n$ for all n.

NOTE. The whole theory of convergence of series of positive terms depends on the study of monotonic sequences. Theorem 4, which follows immediately, and Theorem 19, which comes in a later chapter, are the two fundamental theorems of convergence theory.

THEOREM 4. *If* (α_n) *is a monotonic increasing sequence, then*

EITHER *it has a finite upper bound* U, *and* $\alpha_n \to U$,

OR *its upper bound is* $+\infty$, *and* $\alpha_n \to +\infty$.

The main point of this theorem lies in the proof of the fact that a monotonic sequence either converges or diverges—it cannot be merely non-convergent, as are the sequences of Chap. II, § 4.3.

We first consider the case when (α_n) is m.i. and has a finite upper bound U. Put down any positive number ϵ to begin with; then $U-\epsilon < U$ and, by Theorem 3, there is at least one α_N such that

$$U-\epsilon < \alpha_N \leqslant U.$$

[The reader will probably follow the subsequent argument more easily from the figure.]

But $\alpha_{k+1} \geqslant \alpha_k$ for all k, and so
$$\alpha_n \geqslant \alpha_N \quad \text{when } n \geqslant N;$$
while, by the definition of upper bound,
$$\alpha_n \leqslant U \quad \text{for all values of } n.$$

$$U - \epsilon \qquad \alpha_N \qquad \alpha_n \qquad U$$

Hence, $U - \epsilon < \alpha_N \leqslant \alpha_n \leqslant U \quad$ when $n \geqslant N$,
and so $0 \leqslant U - \alpha_n < U - (U - \epsilon) = \epsilon$.
That is, $\epsilon > 0$; $\ \exists \ N$. $|U - \alpha_n| < \epsilon$ when $n \geqslant N$,
and, by the formal definition of convergence, $\alpha_n \to U$.
[The explanation of $\epsilon > 0$; $\exists$, etc., is given in Chap. II, § 1.2.]

Now suppose that the upper bound is plus infinity. Then
$$A > 0; \quad \exists \text{ an } \alpha_n, \text{ say } \alpha_N, \text{ that exceeds } A.$$
Moreover, $\alpha_n \geqslant \alpha_N \quad$ when $n > N$,
so that $\exists \ N$. $\alpha_n > A \quad$ when $n \geqslant N$.
By the formal definition of divergence, α_n diverges through positive values, or, as we have agreed to write it (§ 1.3), $\alpha_n \to +\infty$.

COROLLARY 1. *If (α_n) is monotonic increasing, and there is a number M such that*
$$\alpha_n < M \quad \text{for all } n,$$
then the sequence (α_n) converges to some number $U \leqslant M$.

By the definition of upper bound, the upper bound, U say, of (α_n) is a number $\leqslant M$. Also, by the theorem, $\alpha_n \to U$.

COROLLARY 2. *If (α_n) is monotonic decreasing, then*
    EITHER *it has a finite lower bound L, and $\alpha_n \to L$,*
    OR   *its lower bound is $-\infty$, and $\alpha_n \to -\infty$.*

In the next chapter we shall make important applications of these results.

3. Rational and irrational numbers

3.1. When p and q are positive or negative integers, the number p/q is said to be a rational number.

A monotonic increasing sequence, (α_n) say, of rational numbers with a finite upper bound U must, by Theorem 4, converge to U. This number U may or may not be itself a rational number. Our fundamental assumption supposes a least number; it says nothing of a least rational number, and would be a false and foolish one if it did. If the number is not rational we call it an irrational number.

As irrational numbers may come into mathematics when they are not obviously derived in this way, we shall make an assumption, easily proved as a theorem when the theory of real numbers has been considered in full.

ASSUMPTION 2.** *Every irrational number is the limit of a m.i. sequence of rational numbers.*

The proof is given in the appendix.

EXAMPLES III

1. Prove that (α_n) is a monotonic decreasing sequence when α_n is given by

(i) $\left(1+\dfrac{1}{n}\right)^{\frac{1}{2}}$,   (ii) $\left(1+\dfrac{1}{n}\right)^{\frac{1}{2}}-1$,   (iii) $\dfrac{\sqrt{(n+1)}-\sqrt{n}}{\sqrt{n^3}}$.

2. Prove that (α_n) is a monotonic increasing sequence when α_n is given by

(i) $\dfrac{n^n}{n!}$,   (ii) $3n^2-n+2$,   (iii) $an^2-2bn+c$,

where a, b, c are independent of n, $a > 0$, and $3a > 2b$.

3. Prove that $an^2-2bn+c$, where $a > 0$, increases with n once n itself exceeds $(2b-a)/2a$.

4. If (b_n) is a sequence of positive terms, and (a_n) is a monotonic increasing sequence, prove that

$$a_{n+1}(b_1+b_2+\ldots+b_n) \geqslant a_1b_1+a_2b_2+\ldots+a_nb_n.$$

Hence show that, if u_n is defined by

$$u_n(b_1+b_2+\ldots+b_n) = a_1b_1+a_2b_2+\ldots+a_nb_n,$$

then (u_n) is a monotonic increasing sequence.

5. **A worked example.** If $a_{n+1} = +\sqrt{(k+a_n)}$, where $k > 0$, $a_1 > 0$, then the sequence (a_n) is monotonic and converges to the positive root of the equation $x^2 = x+k$.

Let α be the positive root, $-k/\alpha$ the negative root, of the equation. Then

$$a_n^2-a_{n+1}^2 = a_n^2-a_n-k = (a_n-\alpha)(a_n+k/\alpha).$$

Hence, if $a_n > \alpha$, then $a_n > a_{n+1}$, for $a_n + k/\alpha$ is positive; and if $a_n < \alpha$, then $a_n < a_{n+1}$.

Again, $\qquad a_{n+1}^2 = k + a_n, \qquad \alpha^2 = k + \alpha,$

and so $\qquad\qquad a_{n+1}^2 - \alpha^2 = a_n - \alpha.$

Hence $a_{n+1} > \alpha$ if $a_n > \alpha$, and $a_{n+1} < \alpha$ if $a_n < \alpha$.

Let $a_1 > \alpha$; then (a_n) is a m.d. sequence and $a_n > \alpha$ for all n; the lower bound of a_n, say l, $\geqslant \alpha$, and $a_n \to l$ as $n \to \infty$.

Write $a_n = l + b_n$, so that $b_n \to 0$. Then

$$l^2 + 2lb_{n+1} + b_{n+1}^2 = l + b_n + k \quad \text{for all } n,$$

that is $\qquad b_n - b_{n+1}^2 - 2lb_{n+1} = l^2 - l - k \quad \text{for all } n.$

Since $b_n \to 0$, we also have [pp. 36 *et seq.* consider such points more fully] $b_n - b_{n+1}^2 - 2lb_{n+1} \to 0$ as $n \to \infty$. Hence $l^2 - l - k$ must be zero; for if it were equal to y, where $y \neq 0$, then $|b_n - b_{n+1}^2 - 2lb_{n+1}|$ would always be equal to $|y|$ and could not be made less than $|y|$ by any choice of n, which would contradict the statement $b_n - b_{n+1}^2 - 2lb_{n+1} \to 0$.

Hence l is a root of $x^2 = x + k$, and is the positive root since $l \geqslant \alpha$.

Similarly, if $a_1 < \alpha$, then (a_n) is a m.i. sequence and $a_n < \alpha$ for all n; the upper bound of a_n, say u, $\leqslant \alpha$, and $a_n \to u$. As before, we can show that $u^2 = u + k$, and so u, being positive, is the positive root of $x^2 = x + k$.

6.† If $a_{n+1} = k/(1 + a_n)$, where $k > 0$, $a_1 > 0$, the sequence (a_n) converges to the positive root of $x^2 + x = k$.

7. Prove that, if $a_{n+1} = a_n^2 + k - k^2$, $a_1 > 0$, and a_n tends to a finite limit l, then l must be either k or $1 - k$.

8. Let (a_n) be defined as above, with $k \geqslant \frac{1}{2}$ and $a_1 > k$. Prove that $a_{n+1} > a_n$ and hence show that $a_n \to +\infty$.

† Examples 5 and 6 are taken from Bromwich, *Theory of Infinite Series* (London, 1908), p. 17.

CHAPTER IV

SERIES OF POSITIVE TERMS

1. Infinite series

1.1. An expression such as

$$u_1+u_2+\ldots+u_n+\ldots \tag{1}$$

is called an infinite series.

DEFINITION. *The infinite series* (1) *is said to converge, to diverge, or to be non-convergent according as the sequence*

$$s_1, s_2, \ldots, s_n, \ldots,$$

where $\qquad s_n \equiv u_1+u_2+\ldots+u_n,$

converges, diverges, or is non-convergent.

If $s_n \to s$, *then* s *is called the sum of the series.*

1.2. There are a few series whose sums can be determined by elementary methods. Such are those given in Examples I. Most readers will be familiar with the geometric series, which can also be summed by elementary methods. We shall need to refer to this series and so we formulate the following:

THEOREM 5. *The geometric series*

$$1+r+r^2+\ldots+r^{n-1}+\ldots \tag{2}$$

is (i) *convergent when* $-1 < r < 1$ *and its sum is then* $(1-r)^{-1}$;

(ii) *divergent when* $r \geqslant 1$;

(iii) *non-convergent when* $r \leqslant -1$.

Proof. Let $s_n = 1+r+\ldots+r^{n-1}$.

(i) Take any definite value of r *between* -1 and $+1$. Then

$$s_n = \frac{1}{1-r}-\frac{r^n}{1-r},$$

$$s_n-\frac{1}{1-r} = \frac{r^n}{1-r}.$$

By § 3, Chap. I, we can make $|r^n|$, and so also $|r^n/(1-r)|$, as small as we please by taking any n that is sufficiently large.

Hence $\qquad s_n \to \dfrac{1}{1-r}.$

Hence the series (2) is convergent and its sum is $(1-r)^{-1}$.

(ii) Take $r = 1$, so that now

$$s_n = n.$$

The sequence s_n diverges to $+\infty$.

Further, if we take a definite $r > 1$, s_n will be greater than n, and again s_n diverges to $+\infty$.

Hence the series (2) is divergent when $r \geqslant 1$.

(iii) If we put $-r = y$ and make $r \leqslant -1$, then $y \geqslant 1$.

$$\begin{aligned} s_n &= 1 + r + \ldots + r^{n-1} \\ &= 1 - y + y^2 + \ldots + (-)^{n-1} y^{n-1} \\ &= \frac{1 + (-1)^{n+1} y^n}{1 + y}. \end{aligned}$$

If n is even, $= 2m$ say, then

$$s_n = s_{2m} = \frac{1 - y^{2m}}{1 + y};$$

this is zero if $y = 1$ and $\to -\infty$ if y has a fixed value > 1.

On the other hand, if n is odd, $= 2m+1$ say, then

$$s_n = s_{2m+1} = \frac{1 + y^{2m+1}}{1 + y};$$

this is unity if $y = 1$ and $\to +\infty$ if y has a fixed value > 1.

Hence, when $y = 1$ the sequence s_n is merely

$$1, 0, 1, 0, \ldots,$$

and when $y > 1$ the sequence s_n has two distinct sets of terms in it, one of which diverges to plus infinity and the other to minus infinity. In both cases the series is non-convergent.

2. Series of positive terms

2.1. Although there are comparatively few series whose sums we can obtain by elementary methods, there are extensive classes of series for which we can decide whether or not they have a sum, i.e. decide whether their s_n tends to a finite limit or does not. It is with this problem that our work will be concerned.

2.2. If u_n is positive for all n the series (1) is called a series of positive terms. For such a series the sequence (s_n), where

$$s_n \equiv u_1 + u_2 + \ldots + u_n,$$

is monotonic increasing, since

$$s_{n+1} - s_n \equiv u_{n+1} > 0.$$

THEOREM 6. (i) *A series of* POSITIVE *terms*

$$u_1 + u_2 + \ldots + u_n + \ldots$$

is convergent if a number K *can be found such that*

$$s_n = u_1 + u_2 + \ldots + u_n < K \quad \text{for all } n.$$

In such a case $s_n \rightarrow s \leqslant K$.

(ii) *If no such number* K *can be found, then the series is divergent.*

(i) As we have seen, (s_n) is a monotonic increasing sequence. If a number K can be found such that $s_n < K$ for every n, then this m.i. sequence has a finite upper bound $s \leqslant K$. Also, a m.i. sequence with a finite upper bound converges to that bound (Theorem 4).

(ii) In this case the m.i. sequence (s_n) has upper bound $+\infty$, and $s_n \rightarrow +\infty$ (Theorem 4).

COROLLARY 1. *If* $u_1 + u_2 + \ldots$ *is a convergent series of positive terms and if* s *is its sum, then* $s_n < s$.

For $s_n < s_{n+1}$ and, since s is the upper bound of the complete sequence (s_n), $s_{n+1} \leqslant s$.

COROLLARY 2. *If a series of positive terms*

$$u_1 + u_2 + \ldots$$

is divergent, and N *is any given number, then the series*

$$u_{N+1} + u_{N+2} + u_{N+3} + \ldots$$

is also divergent.

From the theorem, a series of POSITIVE terms must be either convergent or divergent. If the second series were convergent we could find K so that

$$u_{N+1} + u_{N+2} + \ldots + u_{N+p} < K \quad \text{for all } p.$$

We could then say that

$$s_n = u_1 + u_2 + \ldots + u_n < K + u_1 + u_2 + \ldots + u_N \quad \text{for all } n.$$

Since the R.H.S. of this would be a definite number independent of n, the series $u_1 + u_2 + \ldots$ would be convergent.

2.3. We go on to consider various ways of finding out whether, in the case of a given series of positive terms, there is or is not a number K such that $s_n < K$ for all n. One of these ways is to prove, by special procedure, that certain standard series are convergent, and then to compare other series with them.

We conclude this chapter by considering one such standard series.

3. A standard series

3.1. THEOREM 7. *The series*

$$1^{-p} + 2^{-p} + 3^{-p} + \ldots + n^{-p} + \ldots \tag{3}$$

is convergent if $p > 1$, divergent if $p \leqslant 1$.

Let $p > 1$. Then

$$\frac{1}{2^p} + \frac{1}{3^p} < \frac{2}{2^p} = 2^{1-p},$$

$$\frac{1}{4^p} + \frac{1}{5^p} + \frac{1}{6^p} + \frac{1}{7^p} < \frac{4}{4^p} = 4^{1-p},$$

$$\frac{1}{8^p} + \frac{1}{9^p} + \ldots + \frac{1}{15^p} < \frac{8}{8^p} = 8^{1-p},$$

and so on. Hence the sum of the first

$$1 + 2 + 4 + \ldots + 2^m = 2^{m+1} - 1$$

terms of (3) is less than

$$1 + 2^{1-p} + 4^{1-p} + \ldots + (2^m)^{1-p}. \tag{4}$$

If we write $p = 1 + k$, so that $k > 0$ and $2^{-k} < 1$, (4) becomes

$$1 + \frac{1}{2^k} + \frac{1}{2^{2k}} + \ldots + \frac{1}{2^{mk}} = \frac{1 - (\frac{1}{2})^{k(m+1)}}{1 - (\frac{1}{2})^k}$$

$$< 1/\{1 - (\tfrac{1}{2})^k\}.$$

If n is any given number, we can choose m so that

$$n < 1 + 2 + 4 + \ldots + 2^m,$$

and hence, if s_n is the sum of the first n terms of (3),

$$s_n < 1/\{1 - (\tfrac{1}{2})^k\}.$$

Since this last expression is independent of n, there is a number K, namely $1/\{1 - (\frac{1}{2})^k\}$, such that

$$s_n < K \quad \text{for all } n.$$

Therefore, by Theorem 6,† $s_n \to$ a limit $s \leqslant K$. That is, the series (3) is convergent.

† Instead of referring to Theorem 6, we may say that (s_n) is m.i., and so, by Theorem 4, $s_n \to s \leqslant K$. Some teachers prefer the direct appeal to the properties of monotonic sequences.

Now suppose $p = 1$, so that the series in question is

$$1 + \tfrac{1}{2} + \tfrac{1}{3} + \dots. \tag{5}$$

Since

$$\tfrac{1}{3} + \tfrac{1}{4} > 2 \cdot \tfrac{1}{4} = \tfrac{1}{2},$$

$$\tfrac{1}{5} + \tfrac{1}{6} + \tfrac{1}{7} + \tfrac{1}{8} > 4 \cdot \tfrac{1}{8} = \tfrac{1}{2},$$

$$\tfrac{1}{9} + \tfrac{1}{10} + \dots + \tfrac{1}{16} > 8 \cdot \tfrac{1}{16} = \tfrac{1}{2},$$

and so on,

$$1 + \frac{1}{2} + \left(\frac{1}{3} + \frac{1}{4} \right) + \dots + \left(\frac{1}{2^{m-1}+1} + \dots + \frac{1}{2^m} \right) \tag{6}$$

$$> 1 + \tfrac{1}{2}m.$$

Now (6) contains the first

$$1 + 1 + 2 + 2^2 + \dots + 2^{m-1} = 2^m$$

terms of (5). Hence, if s_n is the sum of the first n terms of (5),

$$s_n > 1 + \tfrac{1}{2}m \quad \text{when } n \geqslant 2^m.$$

If we put down any positive number A, we can choose an integer m so that $1 + \tfrac{1}{2}m$ exceeds A. Then, if we take $n \geqslant 2^m$, s_n exceeds A. Hence the series (5) is divergent.

Finally, if $p < 1$, then

$$n^{-p} > n^{-1}.$$

Hence

$$s_n = 1^{-p} + 2^{-p} + \dots + n^{-p}$$

$$> 1 + 2^{-1} + \dots + n^{-1},$$

and whatever positive number A we put down, s_n will exceed A if $n \geqslant 2^m$ and m is chosen so that $1 + \tfrac{1}{2}m > A$. Hence the series (3) diverges if $p < 1$.

3.2. Alternative proof of Theorem 7.

Theorem 7 may also be regarded as an example of the integral test (Chapter XIV). The use of the integral test provides the simplest proof of the theorem. But this proof uses properties of logarithms and theorems in the calculus that we do not wish to use until we have obtained an independent development of them. If we used the integral test now, we should be in danger of employing Theorem 7 to develop later theorems upon which the properties of logarithms will depend—our argument would then complete a circle.

At this stage, n^{-p} is defined only for rational values of p; when r and s are integers, $n^{-r/s} = 1 / \sqrt[s]{n^r}$.

CHAPTER V

THE COMPARISON TEST; THE RATIO TESTS

1. The comparison test

1.1. We shall, from now on, use the notations

$$\sum u_n, \qquad \sum_{n=1}^{\infty} u_n$$

to denote the infinite series

$$u_1 + u_2 + \ldots + u_n + \ldots.$$

In this section we compare two series $\sum u_n$, $\sum v_n$, wherein each u_n and each v_n is positive.

THEOREM 8. (a) *If* $\sum v_n$ *is a given convergent series of* POSITIVE TERMS *whose sum is* V, *and the terms of* $\sum u_n$ *are such that*

$$0 < u_n \leqslant Kv_n \quad \text{for all } n,$$

where K *is a fixed positive number, then* $\sum u_n$ *is convergent and its sum* $\leqslant KV$.

(b) *If* $\sum v_n$ *is a given divergent series of* POSITIVE TERMS, *and the terms of* $\sum u_n$ *are such that*

$$u_n \geqslant Kv_n \quad \text{for all } n,$$

where K *is a fixed positive number, then* $\sum u_n$ *is divergent.*

Proof (a). If $\sigma_n \equiv v_1 + v_2 + \ldots + v_n$, then σ_n is a monotonic increasing sequence: by the hypothesis that $\sum v_n$ has the sum V,

$$\sigma_n < V \quad \text{for all } n.$$

Accordingly, by the hypothesis that

$$u_n \leqslant Kv_n \quad \text{for all } n,$$
$$s_n \equiv (u_1 + u_2 + \ldots + u_n) \leqslant K(v_1 + v_2 + \ldots + v_n)$$
$$= K\sigma_n$$
$$< KV.$$

But (s_n) is a m.i. sequence, and so (Theorem 4) $s_n \to s \leqslant KV$. That is, $\sum u_n$ is convergent and its sum $\leqslant KV$.

Proof (b). With the above notations s_n, σ_n we now have

$$s_n \geqslant K\sigma_n.$$

By the hypothesis that $\sum v_n$ is divergent, σ_n increases indefinitely† and hence s_n does also.

† Compare the definitions in Chap. II, §4.1.

EXAMPLES IV

1. The series $\sum (n+\tfrac{1}{2})^{-2}$ is convergent, the series $\sum (3n-1)^{-1}$ is divergent.

HINT.
$$\frac{1}{(n+\tfrac{1}{2})^2} < \frac{1}{n^2},$$

and (Theorem 7) $\sum n^{-2}$ is convergent. Put $u_n = (n+\tfrac{1}{2})^{-2}$, $v_n = n^{-2}$, and $K = 1$ in the theorem just proved. Again,

$$\frac{1}{3n-1} > \frac{1}{3n},$$

and (Theorem 7) $\sum n^{-1}$ is divergent. Put $u_n = (3n-1)^{-1}$, $v_n = n^{-1}$, and $K = \tfrac{1}{3}$ in the theorem just proved.

2. The series $\sum \dfrac{1}{(2n+1)^3},$ $\sum \dfrac{n}{(3n+2)^3}$

are convergent.

3. The series $\sum \dfrac{n}{(4n-1)^2},$ $\sum \dfrac{1}{(2n-1)^{1/2}}$

are divergent.

1.2. The test in its practical form. In working most examples that can be made to come within the conditions of Theorem 8 it is simpler to use Theorem 9, which we shall now prove. We begin with a lemma that extends the result of Theorem 1.

LEMMA. *If each term of the sequence* (α_n) *is positive and* $\alpha_n \to a$ *finite positive number* α, *then there are positive numbers* H, K *such that*
$$H < \alpha_n < K \quad \text{for all } n.$$

Since $\alpha_n \to \alpha$,
$$\epsilon > 0; \quad \exists\, N \, . \, |\alpha - \alpha_n| < \epsilon \quad \text{when } n \geqslant N.$$

Let N_1 be the value of N when we take $\epsilon = \tfrac{1}{2}\alpha > 0$. Then, when $n \geqslant N_1$, $|\alpha - \alpha_n| < \tfrac{1}{2}\alpha$, and so
$$\alpha - \tfrac{1}{2}\alpha < \alpha_n < \alpha + \tfrac{1}{2}\alpha. \tag{1}$$

From the finite set of positive numbers
$$\alpha_1, \alpha_2, \ldots, \alpha_{N_1-1}$$

we can choose a least (or equal least) and a greatest (or equal greatest): let their respective values be h, k. Then we have
$$0 < h \leqslant \alpha_n \leqslant k \quad (n = 1, 2, \ldots, N_1-1).$$

If we now choose positive numbers H, K so that

H is less than h and $\frac{1}{2}\alpha$,

and $\qquad K$ is greater than k and $\frac{3}{2}\alpha$,

then $\qquad 0 < H < \alpha_n < K \quad$ for all n.

THEOREM 9. *If $\sum u_n$, $\sum v_n$ are two series of* POSITIVE TERMS *such that*

$$\frac{u_n}{v_n} \to L > 0,$$

then the two series are either both convergent or both divergent.

The number L must be finite and NOT ZERO *in all applications of this theorem.*

Proof. By the preceding lemma we can, if

$$\frac{u_n}{v_n} \to L > 0,$$

determine positive numbers H, K such that

$$H < \frac{u_n}{v_n} < K \quad \text{for all } n,$$

that is, such that $Hv_n < u_n < Kv_n$ for all n.

Hence, by Theorem 8 (*a*), if $\sum v_n$ converges, so does $\sum u_n$, and, by Theorem 8 (*b*), if $\sum v_n$ diverges, so does $\sum u_n$. Since $\sum v_n$ *must* either converge or diverge, this proves the theorem. But if L is zero, we cannot use the lemma and the argument fails.

1.3. It is clear, from the proof, that Theorem 9 is a particular case of Theorem 8. It is a most useful practical form of Theorem 8, as the following examples will show. On the other hand, from a theoretical point of view, Theorem 8 needs to be mentioned explicitly because it is not completely covered by Theorem 9. There is no theorem that says 'because u_n/v_n remains less than a fixed number K for all n, the sequence (u_n/v_n) will converge', and so Theorem 8 covers a wider ground than Theorem 9. Moreover, in theoretical questions (cf. Examples VIII) it is Theorem 8 rather than Theorem 9 that is useful.

EXAMPLES V

[Defer the harder examples until pp. 36–38 have been read.]

1. Prove that $\sum u_n$ is convergent when u_n has any one of the values

$$\frac{n+1}{n^3+2}, \qquad \frac{n+1}{n^3-2}, \qquad \frac{n^2+n-1}{n^4}, \qquad \frac{n^2+n-1}{n^4-3n^3+1},$$

$$\frac{(n^2+n-1)^{\frac{1}{2}}}{(n^5-2)^{\frac{1}{2}}}, \qquad \frac{n^4+5n^2-6}{n^6+11}.$$

2. Prove that $\sum u_n$ is divergent when u_n has any one of the values

$$\frac{n+1}{n^2+2}, \qquad \frac{n-1}{n^2-2}, \qquad \frac{n^2+n-1}{n^3}, \qquad \frac{n^2+n-1}{n^3+3n^2-1},$$

$$\frac{(n^2+n-1)^{\frac{1}{2}}}{(n^3-2)^{\frac{1}{2}}}, \qquad \frac{n^4+5n^2-6}{n^5+11}.$$

METHOD FOR EXAMPLES 1 AND 2. Consider the first example,

$$u_n = (n+1)/(n^3+2).$$

We see that u_n is 'about as big' as $1/n^2$ (compare Examples II), and so we put $v_n = 1/n^2$, when $\qquad u_n/v_n \to 1.$

Apply Theorem 9, with $v_n = 1/n^2$.

3. Prove that if $\sum v_n$ is a convergent series of positive terms, $u_n > 0$, and $u_n/v_n \to 0$, then $\sum u_n$ is convergent.

4. Prove, by considering the particular case

$$u_n = n^{-2}, \qquad v_n = n^{-1},$$

that if $\sum u_n$ is a convergent series of positive terms, $v_n > 0$ and $u_n/v_n \to 0$, then $\sum v_n$ is not necessarily convergent. Give an example to show that it may be convergent. $[v_n = n^{-\frac{3}{2}}.]$

2. The ratio tests

2.1. D'Alembert's and Raabe's tests. When we can neither make use of Theorem 9 nor see fairly readily, by examining the form of u_n, whether $\sum u_n$ converges, we use Theorem 10 and if that fails, as it will when $(u_n/u_{n+1}) \to 1$, Theorem 11.

THEOREM 10. $\sum u_n$ *is a series of* POSITIVE TERMS:

$$if \; \frac{u_n}{u_{n+1}} \to l > 1, \; then \; \sum u_n \; is \; convergent;$$

$$if \; \frac{u_n}{u_{n+1}} \to l < 1, \; then \; \sum u_n \; is \; divergent.$$

This is often called d'Alembert's test.

THEOREM 11. $\sum u_n$ *is a series of* POSITIVE TERMS:

$$if \; n\left(\frac{u_n}{u_{n+1}} - 1\right) \to l > 1, \; then \; \sum u_n \; is \; convergent;$$

$$if \; n\left(\frac{u_n}{u_{n+1}} - 1\right) \to l < 1, \; then \; \sum u_n \; is \; divergent.$$

This is often called Raabe's test.

2.2. These and other special tests involving the ratio u_n/u_{n+1} can be proved, each one separately. But the problem of the ratio tests goes rather deeply into the theory of convergence. When, in the history of our subject, various tests had already been devised, two facts were discovered. One was that however far the line of successive ratio tests was carried it could never be exhaustive; it would always be possible to write down a series $\sum u_n$ whose terms were such that no one of the tests already established could say whether $\sum u_n$ were convergent or not. This point we shall not pursue as it would take us too far afield.

The other fact was that most of the proofs of known tests ran along the same lines. Accordingly, a general test was devised from which the special tests could be deduced. This general test—or rather one that is a little short of it in generality —we now give.

THEOREM 12. *Let a divergent series of positive terms*

$$\sum (D_n)^{-1}$$

be given, and let the terms of a series of POSITIVE TERMS $\sum u_n$ *be such that*

$$D_n \frac{u_n}{u_{n+1}} - D_{n+1} \to L.$$

Then $\sum u_n$ *is convergent if* $L > 0$,

$\sum u_n$ *is divergent if* $L < 0$.

Proof (*a*). Suppose first that, with a given divergent series of positive terms $\sum (D_n)^{-1}$, the terms u_n of the series to be investigated are such that

$$D_n \frac{u_n}{u_{n+1}} - D_{n+1} \to L > 0.$$

Then, $\exists\, N$. for all $n \geqslant N$

$$D_n \frac{u_n}{u_{n+1}} - D_{n+1} > \tfrac{1}{2}L \tag{1}$$

(compare Chap. II, § 6). Since u_{n+1} is positive, we may multiply throughout by u_{n+1} and keep the inequality sign (if it were negative the inequality sign would be reversed after the multiplication and become $<$). Hence, when $n \geqslant N$,

$$D_n u_n - D_{n+1} u_{n+1} > \tfrac{1}{2} L u_{n+1}.$$

Write down this inequality for $n = N, N+1, ..., m-1 \ (> N)$, and add: we get

$$D_N u_N - D_m u_m > \tfrac{1}{2} L(u_{N+1} + u_{N+2} + ... + u_m).$$

Hence $s_m = \sum_{r=1}^{m} u_r < \sum_{r=1}^{N} u_r + \frac{2}{L} D_N u_N.$

But, since N is a definite fixed number, the R.H.S. is fixed and definite. Denote its value by K, say. Then, *for all m*,

$$s_m < K.$$

Hence, by Theorem 6,† $s_m \to s \leqslant K$ and $\sum u_n$ is convergent.

Proof (b). Next suppose that the terms u_n of the series to be investigated are such that

$$D_n \frac{u_n}{u_{n+1}} - D_{n+1} \to L < 0.$$

Then (compare Chap. II, §6) $\exists\ N$. for all $n \geqslant N$

$$D_n \frac{u_n}{u_{n+1}} - D_{n+1} \leqslant 0, \qquad (2)$$

and so $D_n u_n \leqslant D_{n+1} u_{n+1}.$

Hence $D_N u_N \leqslant D_{N+1} u_{N+1} \leqslant ...,$

and $u_r \geqslant \frac{1}{D_r} D_N u_N \quad (r \geqslant N).$

Accordingly, if $m > N$,

$$s_m = \sum_{r=1}^{m} u_r \geqslant \sum_{r=1}^{N} u_r + D_N u_N \sum_{r=N+1}^{m} \frac{1}{D_r}.$$

But, by hypothesis, $\sum (D_n)^{-1}$ is divergent and so s_m is a monotonic sequence that increases indefinitely. Hence $\sum u_n$ is divergent.

2.3. The theorem enunciated is all we need to know if we have in view its application as a test to any series $\sum u_n$ that we may encounter. But we have, in fact, proved rather more than we have enunciated.

---

† Or, since (s_n) is a m.i. sequence, $s_n \to s \leqslant K$, by Theorem 4.

In (a) we have nowhere used the divergence of $\sum D_n^{-1}$; our work in the latter half of (a) is easily rewritten so as to prove the theorem:

If $\sum D_n^{-1}$ is a series of positive terms, divergent or not, and there are positive numbers k, N such that

$$D_n u_n - D_{n+1} u_{n+1} \geqslant k u_{n+1} > 0 \quad \text{when } n \geqslant N,$$

then $\sum u_n$ is convergent.

In (b) the latter half of our work proves the theorem:

If $\sum D_n^{-1}$ is a divergent series of positive terms, and there is a number N such that

$$0 < D_n u_n \leqslant D_{n+1} u_{n+1} \quad \text{when } n \geqslant N,$$

then $\sum u_n$ is divergent.

3. Proofs of Theorems 10 and 11

3.1. In Theorem 12 put $D_n = 1$. If

$$\frac{u_n}{u_{n+1}} - 1 \to L, \quad \text{then} \quad \frac{u_n}{u_{n+1}} \to 1 + L,$$

and Theorem 10 follows.

NOTE. If, as sometimes happens, $u_n \leqslant u_{n+1}$ for all values of n, then the series $\sum u_n$ is clearly divergent. For, in such a case,

$$u_1 + u_2 + \ldots + u_n \geqslant n u_1.$$

This fact is USEFUL FOR REMEMBERING THAT IT IS $\dfrac{u_n}{u_{n+1}} \to l$ LESS THAN ONE WHICH GIVES DIVERGENCE.

3.2. In Theorem 12 put $D_n = n$. If

$$n \frac{u_n}{u_{n+1}} - n - 1 \to L, \quad \text{then} \quad n\left(\frac{u_n}{u_{n+1}} - 1\right) \to L + 1,$$

and Theorem 11 follows.

4. A simple explanation of Theorem 10

4.1. The following considerations led to the discovery of Theorem 10 and also help one to remember it.

If $u_n/u_{n+1} \to L$, then, when n is large, u_{n+1} is 'about the same as u_n/L, u_{n+2} about the same as u_n/L^2, and so on: the terms of the series $\sum u_n$ are, once n is large, roughly the same as those of

$$u_n(1 + L^{-1} + L^{-2} + \ldots)'.$$

Hence $L > 1$ will give convergence, $L < 1$ divergence (Theorem 5).

Theorem 10 can, in fact, be proved by refining the above rough idea into a precise argument.

EXAMPLES VI

1. Prove that each of the series

$$\sum (n+1)x^n, \qquad \sum \frac{n+1}{n+2}x^n, \qquad \sum \frac{(n+1)}{(n+2)(n+3)}x^n$$

converges when $0 < x < 1$, but diverges when $x = 1$ (Theorem 9).

2. Prove that the series

$$1 + \frac{a.b}{c.d}x + \frac{a(a+1)b(b+1)}{c(c+1)d(d+1)}x^2 + \dots \quad (a,b,c,d > 0)$$

converges when $0 < x < 1$ (Theorem 10), that it converges when $x = 1$ provided that $c+d > a+b+1$, and that it diverges when $x = 1$ provided that $c+d < a+b+1$ (Theorem 11).

3. Prove that each of the series

$$1 + x + \frac{x^2}{2!} + \frac{x^3}{3!} + \dots,$$

$$x + \frac{x^3}{3!} + \frac{x^5}{5!} + \dots$$

converges for all positive values of x. [Use Example 10 (i).]

4. Show that $\sum n!x^n$ cannot converge for any positive value of x.

5. Show that the series $\sum n^k x^n$ converges when k is any fixed number and $0 < x < 1$.

6. Show that the series

$$1 + \frac{a}{2}x + \frac{a+1}{2.4}x^2 + \frac{a+2}{2.4.6}x^3 + \dots \quad (a > 0)$$

converges for any positive value of x, and that the series

$$1 + \frac{a}{2}x + \frac{2(a+1)}{2.4}x^2 + \frac{3(a+2)}{2.4.6}x^3 + \dots \quad (a > 0)$$

also converges for any positive value of x. [Use Example 10 (i)].

7. Show that the series

$$1 + \frac{a}{b}x + \frac{2(a+1)}{b^2}x^2 + \dots \quad (a,b > 0)$$

converges when $0 < x < b$ and diverges when $x \geqslant b$.

8. Show that $\sum (a+n)x^n/(b+n)$ is convergent when $0 < x < 1$, divergent when $x \geqslant 1$.

9. Prove, from §2.3 or otherwise, that $\sum u_n$ is divergent if $u_n > 0$ and

either (i) $u_n \leqslant u_{n+1}$,   or (ii) $n\{(u_n/u_{n+1})-1\} \leqslant 1$,

when $n \geqslant$ a fixed N.

10. Prove, from § 2.3 or otherwise, that $\sum u_n$ is convergent (i) if $(u_n/u_{n+1}) \to \infty$, (ii) if $n\{(u_n/u_{n+1})-1\} \to \infty$, (iii) if either of these expressions is always greater than a fixed number k, itself greater than unity.

11. Discuss the convergence of the series

$$\frac{1}{2}x + \frac{1.3}{2.5}x^2 + \frac{1.3.5}{2.5.8}x^3 + \frac{1.3.5.7}{2.5.8.11}x^4 + \dots.$$

12. Prove that each of the series

$$\sum \frac{1.2\dots n}{3.5\dots(2n+1)}x^n, \qquad \sum \frac{1.2\dots(n+1)}{3.5\dots(2n-1)}x^n.$$

converges when $0 < x < 2$ and diverges when $x \geqslant 2$.

13. Prove that each of the series

$$\sum \frac{1.2\dots n}{5.7\dots(2n+3)}x^n, \qquad \sum \frac{1.2\dots n}{7.9\dots(2n+3)}x^n$$

converges when $0 < x \leqslant 2$ and diverges when $x > 2$.

14. Prove that the series

$$\sum \frac{1.2\dots n}{4.7\dots(3n+1)}x^n$$

converges when $0 < x < 3$ and diverges when $x \geqslant 3$, and that

$$\sum \frac{1.2\dots n}{7.10\dots(3n+4)}x^n$$

converges when $0 < x \leqslant 3$ and diverges when $x > 3$.

15. Construct series that

(i) converge when $0 < x < 4$ and diverge when $x \geqslant 4$;

(ii) converge when $0 < x \leqslant 4$ and diverge when $x > 4$.

CHAPTER VI

THEOREMS ON LIMITS

1. Limit theorems

1.1. The following formal theorems on limits have been deferred as long as possible. They will be frequently used from now on.

Let two sequences (α_n), (β_n) be given; let
$$\alpha_n \to \alpha, \qquad \beta_n \to \beta.$$
Then $\alpha_n + \beta_n \to \alpha + \beta, \qquad \alpha_n - \beta_n \to \alpha - \beta, \qquad \alpha_n \beta_n \to \alpha\beta,$
$$\alpha_n / \beta_n \to \alpha/\beta, \quad provided \ \beta \neq 0.$$

The proofs are as follows:

By definition (Chap. II, §2) $\alpha_n - \alpha \to 0$, $\beta_n - \beta \to 0$; that is, $\alpha_n - \alpha$ and $\beta_n - \beta$ can each be made as small as we please by taking any n that is sufficiently large (form A of definition). Hence $(\alpha_n \pm \beta_n) - (\alpha \pm \beta)$ can each be made as small as we please by taking any n that is sufficiently large.

1.2. Using form C of definition, we may write the proof thus:
$$\epsilon > 0; \quad \exists \ N_1 \ . \ |\alpha_n - \alpha| < \tfrac{1}{2}\epsilon \quad \text{when } n \geqslant N_1,$$
and
$$\exists \ N_2 \ . \ |\beta_n - \beta| < \tfrac{1}{2}\epsilon \quad \text{when } n \geqslant N_2.$$
Let N exceed both N_1 and N_2. Then, if $n \geqslant N$,
$$|(\alpha_n + \beta_n) - (\alpha + \beta)| \leqslant |\alpha_n - \alpha| + |\beta_n - \beta| < \epsilon.$$
Hence
$$\epsilon > 0; \quad \exists \ N \ . \ |(\alpha_n + \beta_n) - (\alpha + \beta)| < \epsilon \quad \text{when } n \geqslant N,$$
and this proves that $\alpha_n + \beta_n \to \alpha + \beta$.

1.3. Again, it is easy enough to see, in a rough sort of way, that if α_n approaches (Chap. I, §2) α, and β_n approaches β, then their product $\alpha_n \beta_n$ approaches $\alpha\beta$. We now give a careful proof of this.

2. A useful detail of technique

We want to show that
$$\epsilon > 0; \quad \exists \ N \ . \ |\alpha\beta - \alpha_n \beta_n| < \epsilon \quad \text{when } n \geqslant N,$$
that is to say, putting down any positive ϵ to begin with, we can then find N such that, etc.

It is found, by experience, that in exercises of this sort it pays to put down *two* arbitrary positive numbers, ϵ and k, to begin with and then later on to give k a definite value.

In the present exercise the detail is as follows:

Since $\alpha_n \to \alpha$, $\beta_n \to \beta$, it follows that

$$\epsilon, k > 0; \quad \exists \ N_1 \ . \ |\alpha - \alpha_n| < \epsilon/k \quad \text{when } n \geqslant N_1,$$
$$\text{and} \quad \exists \ N_2 \ . \ |\beta - \beta_n| < \epsilon/k \quad \text{when } n \geqslant N_2.$$

(Notice that we have put ϵ/k instead of ϵ in form C of the definition of convergence; Chap. II, § 2.)

Let N exceed both N_1 and N_2. Then, when $n \geqslant N$,

$$
\begin{aligned}
|\alpha\beta - \alpha_n\beta_n| &= |\alpha(\beta - \beta_n) + \beta_n(\alpha - \alpha_n)| \\
&\leqslant |\alpha(\beta - \beta_n)| + |\beta_n(\alpha - \alpha_n)| \\
&< \frac{\epsilon}{k}\{|\alpha| + |\beta_n|\}.
\end{aligned}
$$

But the sequence (β_n) is convergent and therefore (Theorem 1) it is bounded; that is, there is a number K such that

$$|\beta_n| < K \quad \text{for all } n.$$

Hence, when $n \geqslant N$,

$$|\alpha\beta - \alpha_n\beta_n| < \frac{\epsilon}{k}\{|\alpha| + K\}.$$

Now give k a definite value greater than $K + |\alpha|$, and we have at once

$$|\alpha\beta - \alpha_n\beta_n| < \epsilon \quad \text{when } n \geqslant N.$$

We have thus proved that

$$\epsilon > 0; \quad \exists \ N \ . \ |\alpha\beta - \alpha_n\beta_n| < \epsilon \quad \text{when } n \geqslant N.$$

2.1. We now prove the last of the four results stated in § 1, namely, if $\alpha_n \to \alpha$, $\beta_n \to \beta \neq 0$, then $\alpha_n/\beta_n \to \alpha/\beta$.

Let ϵ, k, N_1, N_2 be the numbers in the beginning of § 2. Then, when $n \geqslant N_1$ and N_2,

$$
\begin{aligned}
\left|\frac{\alpha}{\beta} - \frac{\alpha_n}{\beta_n}\right| &= \left|\frac{1}{\beta\beta_n}\right| \cdot |\alpha(\beta_n - \beta) - \beta(\alpha_n - \alpha)| \\
&\leqslant \left|\frac{1}{\beta\beta_n}\right|\left\{\frac{\epsilon}{k}|\alpha| + \frac{\epsilon}{k}|\beta|\right\}.
\end{aligned}
$$

Since $\beta_n \to \beta \neq 0$, it follows that $|\beta_n| \to |\beta| > 0$ (see **Examples II, 7**).

Let $0 < H < |\beta|$. Then $|\beta_n| > H$ when $n \geqslant$ a certain M and, if N exceeds N_1, N_2, and M,

$$\left|\frac{\alpha}{\beta} - \frac{\alpha_n}{\beta_n}\right| \leqslant \frac{1}{H|\beta|}\frac{\{|\alpha| + |\beta|\}\epsilon}{k} \quad \text{when } n \geqslant N.$$

On choosing $k > \{|\alpha| + |\beta|\}/H|\beta|$, we have

$$\left|\frac{\alpha}{\beta} - \frac{\alpha_n}{\beta_n}\right| < \epsilon \quad \text{when } n \geqslant N.$$

Note that we could not choose k if $|\beta|$ were zero.

COROLLARY. *If* $\alpha_n \to \alpha$, $\alpha_n + A \to \alpha + A$; $A\alpha_n \to A\alpha$; *etc.*

2.2. Method for Examples II. These limit theorems provide a simple procedure for proving the results that were proved in an elementary, but not very simple, way in Chapter II.

The reader will readily prove for himself that

$$a + \frac{b}{n} + \frac{c}{n^2} + \ldots + \frac{k}{n^r} \to a.$$

Hence

$$\frac{an^r + bn^{r-1} + \ldots + k}{\alpha n^r + \beta n^{r-1} + \ldots + \kappa} = \left(a + \frac{b}{n} + \ldots + \frac{k}{n^r}\right)\Big/\left(\alpha + \frac{\beta}{n} + \ldots + \frac{\kappa}{n^r}\right)$$

$$\to a/\alpha \text{ unless } \alpha \text{ is zero.}$$

We work two typical examples from Examples II.

$$\frac{n^2+3}{n^3-1} = \left(\frac{1}{n} + \frac{3}{n^3}\right)\Big/\left(1 - \frac{1}{n^3}\right).$$

The numerator $\to 0$, the denominator $\to 1$. Hence

$$(n^2+3)/(n^3-1) \to 0.$$

$$\frac{3n^2+n}{n^2-5n} = \left(3 + \frac{1}{n}\right)\Big/\left(1 - \frac{5}{n}\right).$$

But

$$3 + \frac{1}{n} \to 3, \qquad 1 - \frac{5}{n} \to 1,$$

and so

$$\frac{3n^2+n}{n^2-5n} \to 3.$$

3. Some theorems about infinite series in general

3.1. It follows at once from § 1 that, if each of the series (not necessarily series of positive terms)

$$u_1 + u_2 + \ldots, \qquad v_1 + v_2 + \ldots$$

is convergent, their sums being U, V respectively, then the series

$$(u_1 + v_1) + (u_2 + v_2) + \ldots$$

is convergent and its sum is $U + V$ (Chap. IV, § 1.1, Definition).

Similarly, $\sum (u_n - v_n)$ will be convergent and have the sum $U - V$.

3.2. On the other hand, $\sum (u_n - v_n)$ or $\sum (u_n + v_n)$ may be convergent when both $\sum u_n$, $\sum v_n$ are divergent. Thus, we can write

$$\sum (u_n - v_n) = \sum u_n - \sum v_n, \qquad \sum (u_n + v_n) = \sum u_n + \sum v_n$$

only when we know that each of $\sum u_n$, $\sum v_n$ is convergent. We shall come back to this point in the examples.

3.3. THEOREM 13. *If, for a given m, the series*

$$u_{m+1} + u_{m+2} + \dots \tag{1}$$

is convergent, then the series

$$u_1 + u_2 + \dots \tag{2}$$

is also convergent. If (1) *has the sum s, then* (2) *has the sum* $u_1 + u_2 + \dots + u_m + s$.

Let s_n denote the sum of the first n terms of (1) and σ_n the sum of the first n terms of (2). Then, when $n > m$,

$$\sigma_n = s_{n-m} + (u_1 + u_2 + \dots + u_m).$$

Also, since m is a given number, $n - m \to \infty$ as $n \to \infty$.

If (1) has the sum s, then $s_n \to s$, and so $s_{n-m} \to s$ as $n \to \infty$. Hence $\sigma_n \to s + u_1 + u_2 + \dots + u_m$.

3.4. One of the occasions when Theorem 13 is useful is in dealing with series of the type we now consider.

Suppose that the series

$$u_1 + u_2 + \dots$$

is not one whose terms are all positive, but is one whose terms are all positive after the mth term, where m is some definite number. We shall speak of such series as one whose terms are *ultimately positive*. (In examples it is rarely of interest to know the value of m; we merely want to know that, sooner or later, such a value of m does occur.) We can apply to the series

$$u_{m+1} + u_{m+2} + \dots$$

the tests for convergence for positive terms and so,

THEOREM 13, COROLLARY. *We can apply the tests for series of positive terms to series whose terms are ultimately positive.*

The following worked examples illustrate some of these points.

Examples VII

1. Discuss the convergence of the series

$$1 - \frac{x-1}{1!} + \frac{(x-1)(x-2)}{2!} - \frac{(x-1)(x-2)(x-3)}{3!} + \cdots$$

for all real values of x.

In the first place, the series terminates if x is a positive integer. The question of convergence does not then arise.

Suppose now that x is not a positive integer. The nth term of the series, u_n say, is given by

$$u_n = (-1)^{n-1}\frac{(x-1)(x-2)\ldots(x-n+1)}{(n-1)!}.$$

Then

$$\frac{u_n}{u_{n+1}} = -\frac{n}{x-n} = \frac{n}{n-x}.$$

Hence u_n and u_{n+1} have the same sign when $n > x$. That is, the terms are *ultimately* one-signed. If they are ultimately positive, we can apply the ratio tests.

If the terms are *ultimately* negative, say $u_n < 0$ when $n > m$, then

$$u_{m+1} + u_{m+2} + \cdots$$

is convergent if $(-u_{m+1}) + (-u_{m+2}) + \cdots$ is a convergent series of positive terms; for if $s_n \to s$ then $-s_n \to -s$.

$$\frac{(-u_n)}{(-u_{n+1})} = \frac{u_n}{u_{n+1}},$$

so that the ratio tests of Chapter V can be applied without change to series of negative terms, or to series whose terms are *ultimately negative*.

Hence, when the terms of a series are ultimately one-signed we can apply the ratio tests.

For any fixed value of x, not an integer,

$$(u_n/u_{n+1}) \to 1$$

and so Theorem 10 tells us nothing. We try Theorem 11:

$$n\left(\frac{u_n}{u_{n+1}} - 1\right) = \frac{nx}{n-x} \to x.$$

Hence the series is convergent if $x > 1$ and is divergent if $x < 1$.

2. Show that $\displaystyle\sum_{n=1}^{\infty} \frac{2n+1}{n^2(n+1)^2} = 1.$

$$\sum_{n=1}^{\infty} \frac{2n+1}{n^2(n+1)^2} = \sum_{n=1}^{\infty} \left\{\frac{1}{n^2} - \frac{1}{(n+1)^2}\right\}.$$

Each of the series $\sum n^{-2}$, $\sum (n+1)^{-2}$ is convergent and so we may write the last expression as

$$\left(1 + \frac{1}{2^2} + \frac{1}{3^2} + \cdots\right) - \left(\frac{1}{2^2} + \frac{1}{3^2} + \cdots\right).$$

By Theorem 13, the first of these is

$$1+\left(\frac{1}{2^2}+\frac{1}{3^2}+\ldots\right).$$

An alternative method which avoids the minor difficulties.

$$\sum_{n=1}^{N}\frac{2n+1}{n^2(n+1)^2} = \sum_{n=1}^{N}\left\{\frac{1}{n^2}-\frac{1}{(n+1)^2}\right\} = 1-\frac{1}{(N+1)^2}.$$

Hence the sum of N terms of the series $\to 1$ as $N \to \infty$; that is,

$$\sum_{n=1}^{\infty}\frac{2n+1}{n^2(n+1)^2} = 1.$$

In all similar examples this is the simplest method to use.

3. Show that
$$\sum_{n=1}^{\infty}\frac{1}{n(n+1)} = 1.$$

Since $\sum n^{-1}$ is not convergent, it would be nonsense to say

$$\sum_{n=1}^{\infty}\frac{1}{n(n+1)} = \sum_{n=1}^{\infty}\left(\frac{1}{n}-\frac{1}{n+1}\right)$$

$$= \sum_{n=1}^{\infty}\frac{1}{n} - \sum_{n=1}^{\infty}\frac{1}{n+1}$$

$$= (1+\tfrac{1}{2}+\tfrac{1}{3}+\ldots)-(\tfrac{1}{2}+\tfrac{1}{3}+\ldots) = 1.$$

The separate brackets $1+\tfrac{1}{2}+\tfrac{1}{3}+\ldots$ and $\tfrac{1}{2}+\tfrac{1}{3}+\ldots$ *look* right enough, but they can have no meaning since these series are divergent.

But the method of dealing with N terms is quite sound, and gives

$$\sum_{n=1}^{N}\frac{1}{n(n+1)} = \sum_{n=1}^{N}\left(\frac{1}{n}-\frac{1}{n+1}\right) = 1-\frac{1}{N+1} \to 1.$$

FURTHER EXAMPLES

4. Show that $\quad \sum_{n=0}^{\infty}\{(n+\tfrac{1}{2})(n+\tfrac{3}{2})(n+\tfrac{5}{2})\}^{-1} = \tfrac{2}{3}.$

5. Prove that $\quad \sum_{n=1}^{\infty}\frac{1}{n^2} = 1 + \sum_{n=1}^{\infty}\frac{1}{n^2(n+1)}.$

6. Prove that $\quad \sum_{n=1}^{\infty}\{n(n+1)\}^{-3} = 10-\pi^2.$

[Assume that $\sum n^{-2} = \tfrac{1}{6}\pi^2.$]

7. Discuss the convergence of the series

$$\sum_{n=1}^{\infty}(-1)^n n!/x(x-1)\ldots(x-n+1)$$

for all real values of x. (Cf. Example 1.)

3.5. *A necessary, but by no means sufficient, condition for the convergence of an infinite series.*

THEOREM 14. *If the series* $\sum u_n$ *is convergent, then* $u_n \to 0$ *as* $n \to \infty$.

Given only that $u_n \to 0$, *it does* NOT *follow that the series* $\sum u_n$ *is convergent.*

Let $\qquad s_n \equiv u_1 + u_2 + \ldots + u_n$.

Then, since $\sum u_n$ is convergent, $s_n \to$ some finite number s as $n \to \infty$. Equally, $s_{n-1} \to s$ as $n \to \infty$. Accordingly, by § 1,

$$u_n \equiv s_n - s_{n-1} \to s - s = 0.$$

On the other hand,

$$1 + \frac{1}{2} + \ldots + \frac{1}{n} + \ldots$$

is a divergent series, although $n^{-1} \to 0$.

EXAMPLES VIII

1. If $\sum u_n$ is a convergent series of positive terms, so also is each of the series $\sum u_n^2$, $\sum u_n u_{n+1}$.

Since $\sum u_n$ is convergent, $u_n \to 0$ as $n \to \infty$. Hence (cf. Chap. II, § 6) $\exists\ N$. $0 < u_n < 1$ when $n \geqslant N$. Accordingly, when $n \geqslant N$,

$$u_n^2 \quad \text{and} \quad u_n u_{n+1} \quad \text{are each less than } u_n.$$

The results follow from the comparison test.

2. If $\sum u_n$ is convergent, then $\sum (u_n - u_{n+1})$ is also convergent and its sum is u_1. (Consider the sum of N terms.)

3. Prove that if $a_n > 0$ and if

$$\frac{a_n}{1 + a_n} \to 0, \quad \text{then} \quad a_n \to 0.$$

By hypothesis (cf. introduction to § 2)

$$\epsilon, k > 0; \quad \exists\ N \ . \ \frac{a_n}{1 + a_n} < \frac{\epsilon}{k} \quad \text{when } n \geqslant N.$$

Hence, when $n \geqslant N$, $\qquad a_n(k - \epsilon) < \epsilon$,

or, on giving k the special value $1 + \epsilon$,

$$a_n < \epsilon.$$

Hence, $\qquad \epsilon > 0; \quad \exists\ N \ . \ a_n < \epsilon \quad \text{when } n \geqslant N.$

(We put down two arbitrary numbers ϵ, k to begin with, and, at our convenience, make a special choice of k: this leaves the one number ϵ arbitrary, and so our final statement is: 'On putting down any arbitrary positive number ϵ to begin with, there is a number N such that $a_n < \epsilon$ when $n \geqslant N$.')

4. Prove that if $a_n \to 0$, then $a_n/(1+a_n) \to 0$.

If $a_n \to 0$, then $1+a_n \to 1$ and (§1) their quotient $\to 0$.

5. Prove that if $a_n > 0$ and if one of the series

$$\sum a_n, \qquad \sum a_n/(1+a_n)$$

is convergent, then so is the other.

HINT. If the second series converges, then $1+a_n \to 1$ and $1+a_n < \frac{3}{2}$ when n is large enough. Use comparison test.

6. If one of the series in Example 5 is divergent, then so is the other.

HINT. *First solution.* A series of positive terms must either diverge or converge.

Second solution. Unless $a_n/(1+a_n) \to 0$, a_n cannot $\to 0$, and neither series can converge.

If $a_n \to 0$, then $1 < 1+a_n < \frac{3}{2}$ when n is large enough. Use comparison test.

7. Prove that in Examples 3–6 $1+a_n$ can be replaced by $c+a_n$, where $c > 0$.

8. If $c > 0$, $a_n > 0$, prove that the series

$$\sum a_n^{-1}, \qquad \sum (a_n+c)^{-1}$$

are either both convergent or both divergent.

HINT. Either $a_n \to \infty$ or it does not. Consider each case.

9. If $\sum u_n = s$, $\sum u_n^2 = S$, $\sum u_n u_{n+1} = \sigma$, and $u_n > 0$, prove that

$$s^2 > S, \qquad s^2 > 2\sigma.$$

10. Give examples to show that $\sum u_n$ may diverge while $\sum u_n^2$ converges.

11. If $u_n > 0$ and $\sum u_n$ is convergent, with sum s, prove that

$$\frac{u_n}{u_1+\ldots+u_n} < \frac{2u_n}{s}$$

when n is sufficiently large. Hence prove that $\sum u_n/(u_1+\ldots+u_n)$ is convergent when $\sum u_n$ is convergent.

12. **Pringsheim's theorem.** If $u_n \geqslant u_{n+1} > 0$ and $\sum u_n$ is convergent, then $nu_n \to 0$.

Let s be the sum, and let $s_n \equiv u_1+\ldots+u_n$.

Then $s_n \to s$ and also $s_{2n} \to s$. Hence

$$u_{n+1}+\ldots+u_{2n} \to 0.$$

But $u_{n+1} \geqslant u_{n+2} \geqslant \ldots \geqslant u_{2n}$, and so $nu_{2n} \to 0$. Hence

$$2nu_{2n} \to 0.$$

But $u_{2n+1} \leqslant u_{2n}$, so that we also have $2nu_{2n+1} \to 0$, and finally, since $\{(2n+1)/2n\} \to 1$,

$$(2n+1)u_{2n+1} \to 0.$$

13. In Example 11, if $\sum u_n$ is divergent, then so is $\sum u_n/s_n$.

Solution. If $n < m$, then, since $s_n = u_1 + \ldots + u_n$ and is m.i.,

$$\frac{u_n}{s_n} + \ldots + \frac{u_m}{s_m} > \frac{u_n + \ldots + u_m}{s_m} = \frac{s_m - s_{n-1}}{s_m}.$$

If $s_m \to \infty$ as $m \to \infty$, the last expression $\to 1$ as $m \to \infty$ when n is fixed.

Hence, with any given n, we can find an m such that

$$\frac{u_n}{s_n} + \ldots + \frac{u_m}{s_m} > \frac{1}{2},$$

and $\sum (u_n/s_n)$ consists of blocks of terms whose sums each exceed $\frac{1}{2}$.

4. Further tests for series of positive terms. Cauchy's test

4.1. THEOREM 15. *If u_n is always* POSITIVE *and $\sqrt[n]{u_n} \to L$, then the series $\sum u_n$ is convergent when $L < 1$, divergent when $L > 1$.*

Proof. (i) Let $L < 1$, and let L_1 be any definite number such that $L < L_1 < 1$. Then (compare Chap. II, § 6)

$$\exists\ N\ .\ \sqrt[n]{u_n} < L_1 \quad \text{when } n \geqslant N,$$

i.e. $u_n < L_1^n.$

But, since $L_1 < 1$, the series

$$L_1^N + L_1^{N+1} + \ldots$$

is convergent, and so, by the comparison test,

$$u_N + u_{N+1} + \ldots$$

is convergent.

Hence (Theorem 13) $\sum u_n$ is convergent.

(ii) Let $L > 1$. Then

$$\exists\ N\ .\ \sqrt[n]{u_n} > 1 \quad \text{when } n \geqslant N.$$

That is, $u_n > 1$ when $n \geqslant N$, so that u_n does not tend to zero. Hence (Theorem 14) $\sum u_n$ is not convergent. But a series of POSITIVE terms must either converge or diverge, and so $\sum u_n$ is divergent.

COROLLARY. *If $a_n > 0$ and $\sqrt[n]{a_n} \to R^{-1}$, then $\sum a_n x^n$ is convergent when $0 < x < R$.*

5. The condensation test

5.1. THEOREM 16. *If $\phi(n) > 0$ and the sequence $\phi(n)$ is monotonic decreasing, then the two series*

$$\sum_{n=1}^{\infty} \phi(n), \qquad \sum_{n=1}^{\infty} h^n \phi(h^n),$$

where h is a positive integer greater than unity, converge or diverge together.

Since $\phi(n)$ is m.d., we have

$$\phi(h)+\phi(h+1)+\ldots+\phi(h^2-1) \leqslant (h^2-h)\phi(h),$$
$$\phi(h^2)+\phi(h^2+1)+\ldots+\phi(h^3-1) \leqslant (h^3-h^2)\phi(h^2),$$
$$\cdot \quad \cdot \quad \cdot \quad \cdot \quad \cdot \quad \cdot \quad \cdot \quad \cdot \quad \cdot$$

By adding these inequalities we get

$$\phi(h)+\phi(h+1)+\ldots+\phi(h^{n+1}-1)$$
$$\leqslant (h-1)\{h\phi(h)+h^2\phi(h^2)+\ldots+h^n\phi(h^n)\}.$$

Suppose that $\sum h^n \phi(h^n)$ is convergent and has the sum S. Then (Theorem 6, Corollary 1), for all values of n,

$$h\phi(h)+h^2\phi(h^2)+\ldots+h^n\phi(h^n) < S.$$

Hence, whatever the value of m,

$$\phi(h)+\phi(h+1)+\ldots+\phi(h+m) < (h-1)S$$

(we can choose n to make $h^{n+1}-1 > h+m$), and the convergence of

$$\phi(1)+\phi(2)+\ldots+\phi(h)+\phi(h+1)+\ldots$$

follows.

Again, on making a slightly different start so as to reverse the inequality signs, we have

$$\phi(h+1)+\phi(h+2)+\ldots+\phi(h^2) \geqslant (h^2-h)\phi(h^2),$$
$$\phi(h^2+1)+\phi(h^2+2)+\ldots+\phi(h^3) \geqslant (h^3-h^2)\phi(h^3),$$
$$\cdot \quad \cdot \quad \cdot \quad \cdot \quad \cdot \quad \cdot \quad \cdot \quad \cdot \quad \cdot$$

By adding these inequalities we get

$$\phi(h+1)+\phi(h+2)+\ldots+\phi(h^n)$$
$$\geqslant \{(h-1)/h\}\{h^2\phi(h^2)+h^3\phi(h^3)+\ldots+h^n\phi(h^n)\}.$$

Suppose that $\sum h^n \phi(h^n)$ is divergent. Then, as the last inequality shows, the sum

$$\phi(1) + \phi(2) + \ldots + \phi(n)$$

increases indefinitely. Hence $\sum \phi(n)$ is divergent.

We have thus shown that the convergence or divergence of $\sum h^n \phi(h^n)$ implies the corresponding property for $\sum \phi(n)$. Also, if $\sum \phi(n)$ is convergent, then $\sum h^n \phi(h^n)$ cannot be divergent, for if it were, $\sum \phi(n)$ would be divergent also; and if $\sum \phi(n)$ is divergent, then $\sum h^n \phi(h^n)$ cannot be convergent.

5.2. The condensation test is particularly well adapted to series that involve logarithms.

For the benefit of those readers who want the principal results as soon as possible we give here a theorem involving logarithms. We shall not use it in this book until after our own treatment of logarithms.

THEOREM 17. *The series*

$$\sum_{n=2}^{\infty} \frac{1}{n(\log n)^k}$$

is convergent if $k > 1$, divergent if $k \leqslant 1$.

If $\phi(n) = 1/n(\log n)^k$ and $h > 1$, then

$$h^n \phi(h^n) = \frac{h^n}{h^n (n \log h)^k} = \frac{1}{n^k (\log h)^k}.$$

Theorem 17 now follows from Theorem 7.

EXAMPLES IX

1. Show that the convergence of $\sum n^{-k}$ when $k > 1$ follows from the convergence of $\sum r^n$ when $r < 1$.

2. Show that $\sum (n \log n)^{-1} (\log\log n)^{-k}$ is convergent if $k > 1$, divergent if $k \leqslant 1$.

3. Find for what sets of values of a, b, c the series

$$\sum n^a (\log n)^b (\log\log n)^c$$

is convergent.

CHAPTER VII

ALTERNATING SERIES

1. Alternating series

1.1. There is one type of series other than series of positive terms for which it is easy to decide whether or not it converges. This type is

$$u_1 - u_2 + u_3 - u_4 + ..., \tag{1}$$

where each u_r is positive. Such a series is called an alternating series, because the signs alternate.

THEOREM 18. *The alternating series* (1) *is convergent if*

(i) u_n *is monotonic decreasing, i.e.* $u_n \geqslant u_{n+1}$,

and (ii) $u_n \to 0$ *as* $n \to \infty$.

We prove this theorem by considering separately the sum of an even number of terms and the sum of an odd number of terms.

$$s_{2n} = (u_1 - u_2) + ... + (u_{2n-1} - u_{2n}),$$

and so, by hypothesis (i), the sequence

$$s_2, \ s_4, \ ..., \ s_{2n}, ... \tag{2}$$

is m.i. (monotonic increasing); but we may write

$$s_{2n} = u_1 - (u_2 - u_3) - ... - (u_{2n-2} - u_{2n-1}) - u_{2n},$$

so that s_{2n} is never greater than u_1. Hence (Theorem 4, Corollary 1)

$$s_{2n} \to L \leqslant u_1. \tag{3}$$

Next consider an odd number of terms. We have

$$s_{2n+1} = u_1 - (u_2 - u_3) - ... - (u_{2n} - u_{2n+1}),$$

so that the sequence

$$s_1, \ s_3, \ ..., \ s_{2n+1}, ... \tag{4}$$

is m.d. (monotonic decreasing); but we may write

$$s_{2n+1} = (u_1 - u_2) + (u_3 - u_4) + ... + (u_{2n-1} - u_{2n}) + u_{2n+1},$$

so that s_{2n+1} is never less than $u_1 - u_2$. Hence

$$s_{2n+1} \to L' \geqslant u_1 - u_2. \tag{5}$$

Accordingly, *without using hypothesis* (ii), we have shown

(A) that the sequence formed by the sums of an even number of terms

$$s_2, \ s_4, \ ..., \ s_{2n}, ...$$

is m.i. and converges to a limit between $u_1 - u_2$ ($= s_2$) and u_1;

(B) that the sequence formed by the sums of an odd number of terms
$$s_1, \ s_3, \ ..., \ s_{2n+1}, ...$$
is m.d. and converges to a limit between $u_1 \ (= s_1)$ and $u_1 - u_2$.

Since $s_{2n} \to L$, $s_{2n+1} \to L'$, we have (Chap. VI, § 1)
$$u_{2n+1} = s_{2n+1} - s_{2n} \to L' - L.$$

But, by hypothesis (ii), $u_{2n+1} \to 0$ and so $L' = L$. That is to say, both the sequences tend to the same limit L.

Hence $s_n \to L$ as $n \to \infty$ through all values.

Formally, the last step in the argument may be set out thus:
$$s_{2n} \to L, \qquad s_{2n+1} \to L.$$

Therefore $\epsilon > 0; \ \exists \ N_1 \ . \ |L - s_{2n}| < \epsilon$ when $n \geqslant N_1$

and $\exists \ N_2 \ . \ |L - s_{2n+1}| < \epsilon$ when $n \geqslant N_2$.

Hence $\exists \ N \ . \ |L - s_n| < \epsilon$ when $n \geqslant N$,

and so $s_n \to L$.

EXAMPLES X

1. Show that each of the series
$$1 - \tfrac{1}{2} + \tfrac{1}{4} - \tfrac{1}{8} + ..., \qquad 1 - \tfrac{1}{3} + \tfrac{1}{5} - ...$$
is convergent.

2. Show that $1^{-p} - 2^{-p} + 3^{-p} - ...$ is convergent if $p > 0$.

3. Use each of the two methods of Examples VII, 2, to show that, when $p > 1$,
$$1^{-p} - 2^{-p} + 3^{-p} - ... = (1 - 2^{1-p})(1 + 2^{-p} + 3^{-p} + ...).$$

4. Show that the series
$$\frac{1}{x+1} - \frac{1}{x+2} + \frac{1}{x+3} - ...$$
is convergent for all real values of x other than negative integers.

(If $x > -1$ the series is alternating; if $x < -1$ the terms are *ultimately* alternating in sign; in the latter case use Theorem 13.)

5. Prove that the series
$$x - \frac{x^2}{2} + \frac{x^3}{3} - ...$$
converges if $-1 < x \leqslant 1$. (If $-1 < x < 0$, we have a series of negative terms; use Chapter V.)

6. Prove that
$$1 + \sum_{n=1}^{\infty} \frac{(-1)^{n+1}}{n(n+1)} = 2 \sum_{n=1}^{\infty} \frac{(-1)^{n+1}}{n}.$$

2. Power series

We have found tests for $\sum a_n x^n$ when $a_n > 0$ and $x > 0$.
The easiest way of dealing with negative values of x is to use
the properties of absolute convergence that will be considered
in Chapter IX. But many examples can be dealt with by
Theorem 18. We shall work one of the examples of Chapter V,
Examples VI, and recommend the others as exercises.

Consider $\sum \{(n+1)/(n+2)\}x^n$ when x is negative. Let $x = -y$.
The series becomes

$$-\tfrac{2}{3}y + \tfrac{3}{4}y^2 + \ldots + (-1)^n \frac{n+1}{n+2} y^n + \ldots. \tag{1}$$

If $v_n = (n+1)/(n+2)$, we have

$$v_n - v_{n+1} = \frac{n+1}{n+2} - \frac{n+2}{n+3} = -\frac{1}{(n+2)(n+3)}.$$

Hence the sequence (v_n) is monotonic increasing and we cannot
apply Theorem 18 directly. But we note that $v_n \to 1$. So we
write

$$\frac{n+1}{n+2} = 1 - \frac{1}{n+2}$$

and consider the two series

$$y - y^2 + y^3 - \ldots \tag{2}$$

and

$$\tfrac{1}{3}y - \tfrac{1}{4}y^2 + \tfrac{1}{5}y^3 - \ldots. \tag{3}$$

By Theorem 18, the series (3) is convergent if

$$\frac{y^n}{n+2} \geqslant \frac{y^{n+1}}{n+3} \quad \text{and} \quad \frac{y^n}{n+2} \to 0.$$

These are both satisfied if $y < 1$.

Also (Theorem 5), the series (2) is convergent when $y < 1$.

When we subtract the two convergent series (2) and (3) we
obtain a convergent series; but the series so obtained is (1).

Hence the series (1) is convergent when $0 < y < 1$.

MISCELLANEOUS EXAMPLES ON CHAPTERS I–VII

1. The sequences (a_n), (b_n) are defined by means of the formulae
$$a_{n+1} = \tfrac{1}{2}(a_n+b_n), \qquad b_{n+1} = +\sqrt{(a_{n+1}b_n)},$$
$a_1 = \alpha$, $b_1 = \beta$; and $\alpha > \beta$. Show that (a_n) is m.d., (b_n) is m.i., and that a_n, b_n each tend to the same limit.

HINT (to be used only after failure).
If $a_n > b_n$, then, from (i), $a_{n+1} > b_n$, $a_{n+1} < a_n$; since $a_{n+1} > b_n$, $b_{n+1} > b_n$ from (ii). Further,
$$a_{n+1}^2 - b_{n+1}^2 = \tfrac{1}{4}(a_n+b_n)^2 - a_{n+1}b_n = \tfrac{1}{4}(a_n^2-b_n^2) = \ldots = \frac{1}{4^n}(\alpha^2-\beta^2).$$

2. In Example 1, if $a_1 = \cos\theta$, $0 < \theta < \tfrac{1}{2}\pi$, $b_1 = 1$, find expressions (by induction) for a_n and b_n.
Prove that (a_n) is m.i. and (b_n) is m.d. Show also that a_n, b_n each tend to $\sin\theta/\theta$.

3. Find expressions for the finite sums
$$\text{(i)} \quad 1^2+2^2x+\ldots+(n+1)^2x^n,$$
$$\text{(ii)} \quad \sum_{r=1}^{n} (1+r^2)/r(r+1)(r+2)(r+3).$$
Discuss the convergence of these sums as $n \to \infty$.

4. Prove that each of the series
$$\sum n^{-1}(\log n)^{-2}, \qquad \sum n/(n^3+1)$$
is convergent.

5. Prove that if $a > b > 0$ the series
$$1 + \frac{b}{a+1} + \frac{b(b+1)}{(a+1)(a+2)} + \ldots$$
converges to the sum $a/(a-b)$.

HINT. The series is convergent and its terms are m.d., so that, by Pringsheim's theorem, $nu_n \to 0$. Also (compare the start of Example 17)
$$\frac{a}{a-b} = 1 + \frac{b}{a+1} + \ldots + \frac{b\ldots(b+n-1)}{(a+1)\ldots(a+n)} + \frac{b\ldots(b+n)}{(a+1)\ldots(a+n)}\frac{1}{a-b}.$$

6. Show that the series
$$\sum_{n=1}^{\infty} \left(\frac{1}{n} - \frac{1}{2n+1} - \frac{1}{2n+2}\right)$$
is convergent.

7. Sum to n terms the series whose nth terms are
$$\text{(i)} \quad \frac{1}{n(n+1)(n+2)}, \qquad \text{(ii)} \quad \frac{1}{n(n+1)(n+3)},$$
$$\text{(iii)} \quad n(n+1)(n+2), \qquad \text{(iv)} \quad nx^{n-1}, \qquad \text{(v)} \quad (n^2+1)x^n.$$
Discuss the question of convergence of the corresponding infinite series.

8. If the successive terms of a sequence of real numbers (s_n) are connected by the relation $s_{n+1}^3 = 7s_n - 6$, and if α is any root of the equation $x^3 - 7x + 6 = 0$, prove that $s_n - \alpha$ has the same sign for all values of n.

Prove that

(i) if $s_1 > 2$, s_n is m.d. and $\to 2$,

(ii) if $1 < s_1 < 2$, s_n is m.i. and $\to 2$,

(iii) if $-3 < s_1 < 1$, s_n is m.d. and $\to -3$,

(iv) if $s_1 < -3$, s_n is m.i. and $\to -3$.

9. Discuss the convergence of $\sum \operatorname{sech} nx$, $\sum x^n \operatorname{sech} nx$.

10. Prove that $\sum (-1)^n / \{n + 2 + (-1)^n\}$ is convergent.

11. If $u_n > 0$, $s_n = u_1 + \ldots + u_n$, prove that $\sum u_n$ and $\sum (u_n/s_n)$ are both convergent or both divergent.

12. Discuss the convergence of the series

$$1 + \frac{1}{1+\alpha} x + \frac{1 \cdot 2}{(1+\alpha)(2+\alpha)} x^2 + \ldots .$$

13. If $u_n = \dfrac{1}{n+1} - \dfrac{1}{n+2} + \dfrac{1}{n+3} - \ldots$, show that

(i) the sequence u_n is monotonic,

(ii) $u_0 - u_1 + u_2 - \ldots - u_{2n-1} = 2nu_{2n}$.

14. Prove that $\sqrt{(n^2+1)} - n$ is monotonic and tends to zero. Show that $\sum (-1)^n \{\sqrt{(n^2+1)} - n\}$ is convergent.

15. Prove that $\quad \dfrac{x^3}{2 \cdot 3} + \dfrac{x^5}{2 \cdot 4 \cdot 5} + \dfrac{1 \cdot 3 \, x^7}{2 \cdot 4 \cdot 6 \cdot 7} + \ldots$

is convergent when $0 < x \leqslant 1$.

16. Prove that

$$\sum n(n+1)x^n, \qquad \sum \frac{n(n+3)(n+5)}{(n+1)(n+2)} x^n$$

are convergent when $0 < x < 1$, divergent when $x \geqslant 1$.

17. Prove that, if $m > n$ and n is a positive integer, then

$$\frac{m+1}{m-n+1} = 1 + \frac{n}{m} \frac{m}{m-n+1}$$

$$= 1 + \frac{n}{m} + \frac{n(n-1)}{m(m-1)} + \ldots \quad \text{to } (n+1) \text{ terms.}$$

18. Prove that, when $x > 1$,

(i) n/x^n and N/x^N, where $N = 2^n$, $\to 0$ as $n \to \infty$,

(ii) $(x-1)^{-1} - (x+1)^{-1} = 2(x^2-1)^{-1}$,

(iii) $\dfrac{1}{x+1} + \dfrac{2}{x^2+1} + \dfrac{4}{x^4+1} + \ldots$

converges to the sum $1/(x-1)$.

19. Prove that the sequence (α_n), where
$$\alpha_n = \sqrt{(n+1)} - \sqrt{n},$$
is m.d. and $\to 0$.

20. Prove that, when $0 < x \leqslant 1$,
$$\sum_{n=1}^{\infty} \frac{2n+1}{n^2(n+1)^2} x^n = 1 - \frac{1-x}{x} \sum_{n=1}^{\infty} \frac{x^n}{n^2}.$$

21. Prove that, if y is a given positive number less than unity, the sequence (α_n), where
$$\alpha_n = (a+n-1)y^n/n,$$
is ultimately monotonic decreasing, and that $\alpha_n \to 0$.

22. Prove that the series
$$1 + ax + \frac{a+1}{2} x^2 + \ldots + \frac{a+n-1}{n} x^n + \ldots$$
is convergent when $-1 < x < 1$. Prove, also, that the series is divergent when $x = 1$ and that it is non-convergent when $x = -1$.

PART II

THE GENERAL THEORY OF
INFINITE SERIES

CHAPTER VIII

THE GENERAL CONVERGENCE PRINCIPLE

1. The general convergence principle

1.1. In Chapter II we gave a formal definition of what is meant by the phrase 'the sequence (α_n) converges to α'. In Examples II we showed that certain definite sequences converged to certain definite numbers. But this gives no clue as to how we are to answer the question 'does the sequence (α_n) converge?' Chapter II will give the answer to the question 'does (α_n) converge to α?' only when we know what α is.

When we came to monotonic sequences we found a simple answer to the question 'does a monotonic sequence converge?' The answer was 'yes, if it is bounded'. For example, if (α_n) is m.i. and $\alpha_n \leqslant 100$, then $\alpha_n \to$ some limit that is not greater than 100.

If the sequence (α_n) is not monotonic, then the test as to whether α_n does or does not tend to a limit, the limit not being specified, is contained in Theorem 19. This is a fundamental theorem. Whether or not the proof is mastered on a first reading is a matter of personal taste, but the theorem itself must be.

THEOREM 19. *The necessary and sufficient condition that the sequence (α_n) should converge (to some finite number α) is*

$$\epsilon > 0; \ \exists \ N \ . \ |\alpha_N - \alpha_{N+p}| < \epsilon \ \text{ for all positive integers } p.$$

1.2. The condition is necessary. This is relatively simple to prove. Suppose that $\alpha_n \to \alpha$. Then (see Chap. VI, § 2)

$$\epsilon, k > 0; \ \exists \ N \ . \ |\alpha - \alpha_n| < \epsilon/k \quad \text{when } n \geqslant N.$$

Hence, if p is any positive integer, we have

$$\begin{aligned}
|\alpha_N - \alpha_{N+p}| &= |(\alpha_N - \alpha) + (\alpha - \alpha_{N+p})| \\
&\leqslant |\alpha - \alpha_N| + |\alpha - \alpha_{N+p}| \\
&< 2\epsilon/k.
\end{aligned}$$

Take $k = 2$ and it follows that

$$\epsilon > 0; \ \exists \ N \ . \ |\alpha_N - \alpha_{N+p}| < \epsilon \ \text{ for all positive integers } p.$$

This proves that, if $\alpha_n \to \alpha$, then the condition is necessarily satisfied.

1.3. The condition is sufficient. Preliminary. The proof of this is more difficult and depends upon the following theorem.

THEOREM 20. *If the infinite sequence (α_n) is bounded, it contains at least one sub-sequence that converges to a finite limit.*

Suppose that
$$a \leqslant \alpha_n \leqslant b \quad (n = 1, 2, 3, \ldots),$$
and think of the points a, b and the various points α_n marked off on a straight line. Bisect ab: there is an infinity of points α_n in ab, and so there is an infinity in one at least of the two halves.

Suppose there is an infinity in the left-hand half *only*. Put
$$a_1 = a, \qquad b_1 = \tfrac{1}{2}(a+b),$$
so that $a_1 b_1$ contains an infinity of the α_n. Bisect $a_1 b_1$: there is an infinity of the α_n in one at least of the two halves.

Suppose there is an infinity in the right-hand half. Put
$$a_2 = \tfrac{1}{2}(a_1+b_1), \qquad b_2 = b_1.$$
Continue this process and always make $a_n b_n$ a part (right-hand if possible) containing an infinity of α_n. The construction of $a_n b_n$ from $a_{n-1} b_{n-1}$ is always such that
$$a_n \geqslant a_{n-1}, \qquad b_n \leqslant b_{n-1}.$$
Hence (a_n) is m.i. and, since each $a_n \leqslant b$, $a_n \to L \leqslant b$; also (b_n) is m.d. and, since each $b_n \geqslant a$, $b_n \to L_1 \geqslant a$.

It follows that
$$b_n - a_n \to L_1 - L.$$
But $b_n - a_n = (b-a)2^{-n}$ and tends to zero, so that $L = L_1$.

Since $a_n \to L$ from the left and $b_n \to L$ from the right, we have
$$0 \leqslant L - a_n < b_n - a_n < (b-a)2^{-n},$$
$$0 \leqslant b_n - L < b_n - a_n < (b-a)2^{-n}.$$
(Notice the sign $\leqslant$: from a certain stage onwards a_n or b_n may stay fixed at L.)

Accordingly, if x is any point in $a_n b_n$, then
$$|L - x| < (b-a)2^{-n}.$$

Now let α_{11} be the first member of the sequence (α_n) that lies in $a_1 b_1$, α_{22} the first other than α_{11} that lies in $a_2 b_2$, α_{33} the first other than α_{11} and α_{22} that lies in $a_3 b_3$; and so on.

We then have a sequence (a partial or sub-sequence of the α_n)

$$\alpha_{11}, \quad \alpha_{22}, \quad \alpha_{33}, \ldots$$

such that $|L - \alpha_{nn}| < (b-a)2^{-n}.$

Hence, on writing $\beta_n \equiv \alpha_{nn}$, $\beta_n \to L$ as $n \to \infty$.

Notice that, by its mode of construction, L must lie either inside ab or, in extreme cases, at one or other of a and b; it cannot lie outside ab.

1.4. COROLLARY. *If the infinite sequence (α_n) is bounded, then either it converges or it contains two sub-sequences that converge to different limits.*

As in the theorem, there is one sub-sequence (β_n) that converges to L. Then

EITHER (i) for each and every $\epsilon > 0$, only a finite number (or none) of the α_n are such that $|L - \alpha_n| \geqslant \epsilon$,

OR (ii) for some $\epsilon > 0$, an infinity of α_n are such that

$$|L - \alpha_n| \geqslant \epsilon.$$

If (i) holds, then $\alpha_n \to L$ (by definition of convergence).

If (ii) holds, let λ be a definite positive number such that

$$|L - \alpha_n| \geqslant \lambda \quad \text{for an infinity of } \alpha_n.$$

Let (γ_n) be the sequence we get by omitting from (α_n) all the terms such that $|L - \alpha_n| < \lambda$. Then, if L is neither a nor b (if it is, slight changes are necessary: these we leave to the reader), the sequence (γ_n) lies in $a, L - \lambda$ and $L + \lambda, b$. Moreover, by hypothesis, (γ_n) is an infinite sequence.

Either in $a, L - \lambda$ or in $L + \lambda, b$ there is an infinity of γ_n. We can, as in the theorem, select a sub-sequence which converges to some number L_1, and, as L_1 cannot be *within* $L - \lambda$, $L + \lambda$, L_1 cannot be the same as L.

That is, (α_n) contains two sub-sequences, one of which converges to L and the other to $L_1 \neq L$.

1.5. The condition in Theorem 19 is sufficient. Suppose the condition is satisfied; that is,

$$\epsilon > 0; \quad \exists \; N \; . \; |\alpha_N - \alpha_{N+p}| < \epsilon \quad \text{for all positive˙integers } p.$$

Then, when $m >$ some definite M (the value of N when $\epsilon = 1$),

$$|\alpha_M - \alpha_m| < 1,$$

i.e. $\alpha_M - 1 < \alpha_m < \alpha_M + 1.$

The sequence $\alpha_{M+1}, \alpha_{M+2}, \ldots$ is bounded. Hence (Corollary, Theorem 20) it must either converge or contain two subsequences that converge to two distinct limits L and L_1. But the latter is impossible when our condition is satisfied. For, if possible, suppose there are two such sub-sequences and that $L_1 > L$. Then, if k is a given positive number,

$$\exists \; N \; . \; |\alpha_N - \alpha_{N+p}| < \frac{L_1 - L}{k} \quad \text{for all positive integers } p.$$

Since one sub-sequence $\to L$ and the other $\to L_1$, there are positive numbers q, r such that

$$|L - \alpha_{N+q}| < \frac{L_1 - L}{k}, \qquad |L_1 - \alpha_{N+r}| < \frac{L_1 - L}{k}.$$

It follows that

$$|L_1 - L| = |(L_1 - \alpha_{N+r}) + (\alpha_{N+r} - \alpha_N) + (\alpha_N - \alpha_{N+q}) + (\alpha_{N+q} - L)|$$
$$\leqslant |L_1 - \alpha_{N+r}| + |\alpha_{N+r} - \alpha_N| + |\alpha_N - \alpha_{N+q}| + |\alpha_{N+q} - L|$$
$$< 4(L_1 - L)/k.$$

That is to say, if there were two sub-sequences converging to distinct limits, it would follow, on taking $k = 4$, that

$$L_1 - L < L_1 - L,$$

which is absurd. Hence the sequence (α_n) must converge.

This completes the proof of Theorem 19.

1.6. Complex numbers. Complex numbers will be considered in a later chapter. In all other contexts numbers are supposed to be real unless the contrary is stated.

CHAPTER IX

ABSOLUTE AND NON-ABSOLUTE CONVERGENCE

1. The convergence principle applied to series

The infinite series $\qquad u_1 + u_2 + \ldots$

is convergent if the sequence (s_n), where

$$s_n \equiv u_1 + u_2 + \ldots + u_n,$$

is convergent.

THEOREM 21. *The necessary and sufficient condition for the series $\sum u_n$ to be convergent is*

$$\epsilon > 0; \quad \exists\ N \ . \ |u_{N+1} + \ldots + u_{N+p}| < \epsilon$$

for all positive integers p.

This is an immediate corollary of Theorem 19, for

$$s_{N+p} - s_N \equiv u_{N+1} + \ldots + u_{N+p}.$$

2. Absolute convergence

2.1. DEFINITION. *The series $\sum u_n$ is said to be absolutely convergent if the series $\sum |u_n|$ is convergent.*

THEOREM 22. *If a series is absolutely convergent, then it is also convergent. If a series is convergent it is not necessarily absolutely convergent.*

Suppose $\sum |u_n|$ is convergent. Then

$$\epsilon > 0; \quad \exists\ N \ . \ ||u_{N+1}| + \ldots + |u_{N+p}|| < \epsilon$$

for all positive integers p. But (modulus of sum $\leqslant$ sum of moduli)

$$|u_{N+1} + \ldots + u_{N+p}| \leqslant |u_{N+1}| + \ldots + |u_{N+p}|,$$

and so $\qquad \epsilon > 0; \quad \exists\ N \ . \ |u_{N+1} + \ldots + u_{N+p}| < \epsilon$

for all positive integers p. Hence, by Theorem 21, $\sum u_n$ is convergent.

On the other hand, particular examples show that $\sum u_n$ may be convergent and $\sum |u_n|$ divergent: e.g. $1 - \frac{1}{2} + \frac{1}{3} - \ldots$ is convergent, $1 + \frac{1}{2} + \frac{1}{3} + \ldots$ is divergent. (Cf. Theorems 18, 7.)

2.2. THEOREM 23. (i) *If a series is absolutely convergent, then the series formed by its positive terms alone is convergent, and the series formed by its negative terms alone is convergent.*

(ii) *If a series converges but is not absolutely convergent, then the series formed by its positive (negative) terms alone is divergent.*

Let the series be $\sum a_n$, and let $|a_n| \equiv \alpha_n$. Further, let

$$p_n = \tfrac{1}{2}(a_n + \alpha_n) = \begin{cases} a_n & \text{when } a_n \text{ is positive} \\ 0 & \text{when } a_n \text{ is negative,} \end{cases}$$

$$q_n = \tfrac{1}{2}(a_n - \alpha_n) = \begin{cases} a_n & \text{when } a_n \text{ is negative} \\ 0 & \text{when } a_n \text{ is positive,} \end{cases}$$

$$P_n = p_1 + \ldots + p_n, \qquad Q_n = q_1 + \ldots + q_n,$$
$$s_n = a_1 + \ldots + a_n, \qquad \sigma_n = \alpha_1 + \ldots + \alpha_n.$$

With this notation we have, by easy algebra,
$$P_n = \tfrac{1}{2}(s_n + \sigma_n), \qquad Q_n = \tfrac{1}{2}(s_n - \sigma_n). \tag{1}$$

But if $\sum a_n$ converges absolutely, then $\sigma_n \to$ a finite limit, σ say, and $s_n \to$ a finite limit, s say. Hence
$$P_n \to \tfrac{1}{2}(s + \sigma), \qquad Q_n \to \tfrac{1}{2}(s - \sigma), \tag{2}$$
and (i) follows, since P_n, Q_n are formed respectively from the positive, negative terms alone.

To prove (ii) suppose that the series formed by the positive terms alone is convergent and that the original series is convergent. Then $P_n \to$ a finite limit, P say, and $s_n \to$ a finite limit, s say. It follows, from (1), that
$$\sigma_n \to 2P - s,$$
i.e. the series of absolute values, $\sum \alpha_n$, is convergent.

Hence, if $\sum a_n$ is convergent and $\sum \alpha_n$ is divergent, the series of positive terms alone cannot converge.

2.3. The ratio tests. When, in Chapter V, Examples VI, we considered power series such as
$$1 + 2x + 3x^2 + \ldots, \tag{1}$$
we confined our attention to positive values of x. We now see that this series will converge, whether x is positive or negative, provided that
$$1 + 2|x| + 3|x|^2 + \ldots$$
is convergent. If we write $u_n = (n+1)|x|^n$,
$$\frac{u_n}{u_{n+1}} = \frac{(n+1)}{(n+2)|x|} \to \frac{1}{|x|}.$$
Hence the series (1) is absolutely convergent when $|x| < 1$.

The examples that follow deal with the same series as did Examples VI, but negative values of x are now included.

EXAMPLES XI

1. Prove that each of the series

$$\sum (n+1)x^n, \qquad \sum \frac{n+1}{n+2}x^n, \qquad \sum \frac{n+1}{(n+2)(n+3)}x^n$$

converges when $|x| < 1$, diverges when $x = 1$, and does not converge when $|x| > 1$. Show that the third series is the only one of the three that converges when $x = -1$.

HINT. When $|x| < 1$, consider the series of absolute values and use the ratio tests. When $|x| > 1$, the nth term u_n does not tend to zero, and Theorem 14 proves the result. When $x = -1$, only the terms of the last series tend to zero and the convergence of this series is proved by Theorem 18.

2. Prove that the series

$$1 + \frac{a.b}{c.d}x + \frac{a(a+1)b(b+1)}{c(c+1)d(d+1)}x^2 + \dots \quad (c, d > 0)$$

converges when $|x| < 1$.

3. Prove that each of the series

$$1 + x + \frac{x^2}{2!} + \frac{x^3}{3!} + \dots,$$

$$x + \frac{x^3}{3!} + \frac{x^5}{5!} + \dots$$

converges for all real values of x.

4. Show that $\sum n!x^n$ cannot converge for any real value of x.

HINT. $|u_{n+1}|$ is ultimately greater than $|u_n|$, and so u_n cannot tend to zero.

5. Show that $\sum n^k x^n$ converges when k is any fixed number and $|x| < 1$. Show that it does not converge when $|x| > 1$ and find for what ranges of values of k it will converge when $x = 1$, when $x = -1$.

6. Show that each of the series

$$1 + \frac{a}{2}x + \frac{a+1}{2.4}x^2 + \frac{a+2}{2.4.6}x^3 + \dots,$$

$$1 + \frac{a}{2}x + \frac{2(a+1)}{2.4}x^2 + \frac{3(a+2)}{2.4.6}x^3 + \dots$$

is convergent for all real values of x.

7. Show that the series

$$1 + \frac{a}{b}x + \frac{2(a+1)}{b^2}x^2 + \frac{3(a+2)}{b^3}x^3 + \dots$$

converges when $|x| < |b|$.

3. Abel's and Dirichlet's tests

3.1. Let (a_n), (v_n) be any two sequences, and let
$$s_n \equiv a_1 + a_2 + \ldots + a_n.$$
Then, by simple algebra,
$$a_1 v_1 + a_2 v_2 + \ldots + a_n v_n \tag{1}$$
$$= s_1 v_1 + (s_2 - s_1)v_2 + \ldots + (s_n - s_{n-1})v_n$$
$$= s_1(v_1 - v_2) + s_2(v_2 - v_3) + \ldots + s_{n-1}(v_{n-1} - v_n) + s_n v_n. \tag{2}$$
That is, we have transformed (1) into another shape, namely (2), wherein we 'sum the a's and difference the v's'.

Now suppose that
(i) (v_n) is a m.d. sequence of positive terms,
(ii) the numbers h, H are such that
$$h \leqslant s_r \leqslant H \quad (r = 1, 2, \ldots, n).$$
Then we have†
$$hv_1 = h(v_1 - v_2) + h(v_2 - v_3) + \ldots + h(v_{n-1} - v_n) + hv_n$$
$$\leqslant s_1(v_1 - v_2) + s_2(v_2 - v_3) + \ldots + s_{n-1}(v_{n-1} - v_n) + s_n v_n,$$
that is, by the equality of (1) and (2),
$$hv_1 \leqslant a_1 v_1 + a_2 v_2 + \ldots + a_n v_n.$$
Similarly, $a_1 v_1 + a_2 v_2 + \ldots + a_n v_n \leqslant Hv_1$.

3.2. We now collect these results into an important lemma.

Abel's lemma. *If (v_n) is a monotonic decreasing sequence of positive numbers, and h, H are such that*
$$h \leqslant a_1 + a_2 + \ldots + a_r \leqslant H \quad (r = 1, 2, \ldots, n),$$
then $\quad hv_1 \leqslant a_1 v_1 + a_2 v_2 + \ldots + a_n v_n \leqslant Hv_1.$

In this lemma h or H, or both, may be negative. The notation $a < b$ means that a is algebraically less than b; thus $-3 < -2$. When we use absolute values we need the following result.

Corollary of Abel's lemma. *If (v_n) is a monotonic decreasing sequence of positive numbers, and K is such that*
$$|a_1 + a_2 + \ldots + a_r| \leqslant K \quad (r = 1, 2, \ldots, n),$$
then $\quad |a_1 v_1 + a_2 v_2 + \ldots + a_n v_n| \leqslant Kv_1.$

† Notice that the argument depends on $v_n \geqslant v_{n+1}$. If, for example, $v_2 < v_3$, then $v_2 - v_3$ is negative, and so
$$(v_2 - v_3)h > s_2(v_2 - v_3) \quad \text{when } h < s_2.$$

This follows almost at once from the lemma itself. For we can write the condition $|a_1+a_2+...+a_r| \leqslant K$ as

$$-K \leqslant a_1+a_2+...+a_r \leqslant K,$$

and so, by the lemma,

$$-Kv_1 \leqslant a_1v_1+a_2v_2+...+a_nv_n \leqslant Kv_1.$$

3.3. THEOREM 24. *If (a_n) is a sequence of numbers such that, for some fixed number K,*

$$|a_1+a_2+...+a_n| < K \quad \text{for all } n,$$

and (v_n) is a monotonic sequence that converges to zero, then $\sum a_n v_n$ is convergent.

Suppose, in the first place, that (v_n) is a monotonic decreasing sequence of positive numbers, and that $v_n \to 0$. Then

$$\epsilon, k > 0; \quad \exists N \: . \: 0 < v_n < k\epsilon \quad \text{when } n \geqslant N.$$

[It is a matter of indifference whether we use ϵ times k or ϵ divided by k.]

But, for all positive integers p,

$$\begin{aligned}
|a_{N+1}+a_{N+2}+...+a_{N+p}| \\
= |(a_1+a_2+...+a_{N+p})-(a_1+a_2+...+a_N)| \\
\leqslant |a_1+a_2+...+a_{N+p}|+|a_1+a_2+...+a_N| \\
< 2K.
\end{aligned}$$

Hence, by the corollary of Abel's lemma,

$$\begin{aligned}
|a_{N+1}v_{N+1}+...+a_{N+p}v_{N+p}| &< 2Kv_{N+1} \\
&< 2Kk\epsilon.
\end{aligned}$$

On putting $k = 1/2K$, we see that

$$\epsilon > 0; \quad \exists N \: . \: |a_{N+1}v_{N+1}+...+a_{N+p}v_{N+p}| < \epsilon$$

for all positive integers p. Hence, by Theorem 21, $\sum a_n v_n$ is convergent.

If (v_n) is a monotonic increasing sequence (of negative terms) that converges to zero, $(-v_n)$ is a monotonic decreasing sequence (of positive terms) that converges to zero. As we have proved, $\sum -a_n v_n$ is convergent: hence $\sum a_n v_n$ is convergent.

DEFINITION. *A* SERIES *$\sum a_n$ is said to be* BOUNDED *if there is a constant K such that $|a_1+a_2+...+a_n| < K$ for all n.*

A convergent series is necessarily bounded (by Theorem 1), though not all bounded series are convergent: for example, the sum of any number of terms of the series

$$1-1+1-1+\ldots$$

cannot exceed unity.

3.4. THEOREM 25. *If $\sum a_n$ is a convergent series and (v_n) is a monotonic sequence that tends to a finite limit, then $\sum a_n v_n$ is also convergent.*

The theorem has no interest if $\sum a_n$ is absolutely convergent, for (v_n) is bounded, by hypothesis, and so

$$|a_n v_n| < K|a_n|,$$

say. If $\sum |a_n|$ is convergent, the convergence of $\sum |a_n v_n|$ follows from the comparison test (Theorem 8).

If $\sum a_n$ is convergent but not absolutely convergent, then the positive, negative terms alone form two divergent series. The convergence of $\sum a_n$ is due, so to speak, to the nicety of balance between a diverging positive and a diverging negative. The theorem asserts that this nicety of balance between the positives and negatives is not upset by the introduction of the factors v_n.

Suppose that $v_n \to v$, and that

$$s_n \equiv a_1 + a_2 + \ldots + a_n \to s.$$

Let $w_n = v - v_n$. Then

$$a_1 v_1 + a_2 v_2 + \ldots + a_n v_n = s_n v - (a_1 w_1 + a_2 w_2 + \ldots + a_n w_n).$$

Let
$$\sigma_n = a_1 w_1 + a_2 w_2 + \ldots + a_n w_n.$$

The sequence (s_n) is bounded, since $s_n \to s$ (Theorem 1). Hence there is a number K such that

$$|a_1 + a_2 + \ldots + a_n| < K \quad \text{for all } n.$$

Further, the sequence (w_n) is monotonic and converges to zero. Hence, by Theorem 24, the series $\sum a_n w_n$ is convergent; that is,

$$\sigma_n \to \text{a finite limit, } \sigma \text{ say.}$$

Accordingly,

$$a_1 v_1 + a_2 v_2 + \ldots + a_n v_n = s_n v - \sigma_n$$
$$\to sv - \sigma.$$

Hence the series $\sum a_n v_n$ is convergent.

3.5. Theorem 24 is usually called Dirichlet's test, and Theorem 25 Abel's test. Before we give special examples we note one result, an example on Theorem 24, which is of almost sufficient importance to rank as a theorem.

Let (v_n) be any monotonic sequence that converges to zero. Then $\sum v_n \sin n\theta$ is convergent for all real values of θ, and $\sum v_n \cos n\theta$ is convergent for all real values of θ other than zero and multiples of 2π.

By elementary trigonometry, when θ is real and $\sin \frac{1}{2}\theta \neq 0$,

$$\left| \sum_{r=1}^{n} \cos r\theta \right| = \left| \frac{\sin \frac{1}{2}n\theta \cos \frac{1}{2}(n+1)\theta}{\sin \frac{1}{2}\theta} \right| < \frac{1}{|\sin \frac{1}{2}\theta|},$$

$$\left| \sum_{r=1}^{n} \sin r\theta \right| = \left| \frac{\sin \frac{1}{2}n\theta \sin \frac{1}{2}(n+1)\theta}{\sin \frac{1}{2}\theta} \right| < \frac{1}{|\sin \frac{1}{2}\theta|}.$$

Hence, if $\sin \frac{1}{2}\theta \neq 0$, we may put $K = |\operatorname{cosec} \frac{1}{2}\theta|$ in Theorem 24 both when $a_n = \cos n\theta$ and when $a_n = \sin n\theta$. But $\sin \frac{1}{2}\theta \neq 0$ unless θ is zero or a multiple of 2π. Hence

$$\sum v_n \sin n\theta, \qquad \sum v_n \cos n\theta$$

are convergent unless θ is zero or a multiple of 2π.

When θ is zero or a multiple of 2π, the first series is merely a series of zeros, while the second is $\sum v_n$ and may or may not be convergent.

Examples XII

1. Prove that, of the series

$$\sum \frac{\cos n\theta}{n}, \qquad \sum \frac{\sin n\theta}{n}, \qquad \sum \frac{\cos n\theta}{n^2}, \qquad \sum \frac{\sin n\theta}{n^2},$$

all save the first converge for all real values of θ.

2. Prove that $\sum n^{-k} \cos n\theta$ is convergent for all real values of θ if $k > 1$, and is convergent for all real values of θ other than multiples of 2π (including zero) if $0 < k < 1$.

3. If $\sum a_n$ converges, then $\sum a_n n^{-x}$ converges when $x \geqslant 0$.

4. If x is not a positive integer, then

$$\sum \frac{a_n}{n}, \qquad \sum \frac{a_n}{n-x}$$

are both convergent or both non-convergent.

Solution. If $\sum a_n/n$ converges, write $v_n = n/(n-x)$. Then

$$v_n - v_{n+1} = \frac{x}{(n-x)(n+1-x)},$$

and, when $n > [x]$, this has the sign of x. Hence the sequence (v_n) is ultimately monotonic; also, $v_n \to 1$ as $n \to \infty$. Hence, by Theorem 25,

$$\sum \frac{a_n}{n} v_n = \sum \frac{a_n}{n} \frac{n}{n-x} = \sum \frac{a_n}{n-x}$$

is convergent.

The same method applies if we suppose the second series to be convergent: we then prove that the convergence of the first series follows.

5. The series $\sum (-1)^{n-1}(n-x)^{-1}$ is convergent when x is not an integer.

6. The series $\sum (-1)^n/\sqrt{n}$, $\sum (-1)^n/\sqrt{(x+n)}$ when x is not a negative integer, are both convergent.

7. The series $\sum (-1)^n b_n$ is convergent provided that b_n tends monotonically to zero. (Put $a_n = (-1)^n$ in Theorem 24.)

8. Prove that $\sum \dfrac{\sin(n+\frac{1}{2})x}{n+\frac{1}{2}}$ is convergent for all real values of x.

3.6. The more general forms of Theorems 24 and 25.

The two theorems 24A, 25A that follow are more general than the previous ones and are also applicable when a_n, v_n are complex numbers, but it is not so easy to see whether they apply to any particular series. The new theorems are all but self-evident if we return to the identity of § 3.1 and remember that $\sum a_n$ converges if $\sum |a_n|$ does.

In § 3.1 we proved that

$$a_1 v_1 + a_2 v_2 + \dots + a_n v_n \tag{1}$$

$$= s_1(v_1 - v_2) + s_2(v_2 - v_3) + \dots + s_{n-1}(v_{n-1} - v_n) + s_n v_n, \tag{2}$$

where $s_n \equiv a_1 + a_2 + \dots + a_n$.

Let $\sum |v_n - v_{n+1}|$ be convergent and let $\sum a_n$ be bounded, i.e.

$$\exists\, K\, .\ |s_n| < K \quad \text{for all } n.$$

Then $$|s_n(v_n - v_{n+1})| < K|v_n - v_{n+1}|,$$

and each of the series

$$\sum s_n(v_n - v_{n+1}), \qquad \sum (v_n - v_{n+1}) \tag{3}$$

is convergent. Since $\sum s_n(v_n - v_{n+1})$ is convergent,

$$s_1(v_1 - v_2) + s_2(v_2 - v_3) + \dots + s_{n-1}(v_{n-1} - v_n),$$

i.e. $$(a_1 v_1 + \dots + a_n v_n) - s_n v_n, \tag{4}$$

tends to a finite limit.

Since $\sum (v_n - v_{n+1})$ is convergent,

$$(v_1 - v_2) + (v_2 - v_3) + \ldots + (v_{n-1} - v_n),$$

i.e.

$$v_1 - v_n,$$

also tends to a finite limit; that is, $v_n \to v$, a finite limit.

It follows from (4) that, if

EITHER

$$v_n \to 0$$

OR

$$s_n \to s, \quad \text{a finite limit,}$$

then $(a_1 v_1 + \ldots + a_n v_n)$ tends to a finite limit; for in the first case $|s_n| < K$ and $s_n v_n \to 0$, and in the second case $s_n v_n \to sv$. We now enunciate the theorems that embody these results.

THEOREM 24 A. *If $\sum a_n$ is bounded, $\sum |v_n - v_{n+1}|$ is convergent, and $v_n \to 0$, then $\sum a_n v_n$ is convergent.*

THEOREM 25 A. *If $\sum a_n$ is convergent, and $\sum |v_n - v_{n+1}|$ is convergent, then $\sum a_n v_n$ is also convergent.*

3.7. Worked example. If (v_n) is m.d. and $\sum v_n$ is convergent, then $\sum n(v_n - v_{n+1})$ is convergent and its sum is $\sum v_n$.

To deal with problems of this type, use § 3.1 with $a_n = 1$, so that $s_n = n$. Thus,

$$v_1 + \ldots + v_n = (v_1 - v_2) + 2(v_2 - v_3) + \ldots + (n-1)(v_{n-1} - v_n) + nv_n.$$

In the first place, $v_n \to 0$ since $\sum v_n$ is convergent and so, in the second place, v_n must be positive since (v_n) is m.d. Finally, by Pringsheim's theorem (Examples VIII, 12) $nv_n \to 0$, and the result follows.

CHAPTER X

THE PRODUCT OF TWO SERIES

1. The use of brackets in infinite series

Consider any *sequence* (α_n) that is known to converge to a limit α. Then, confining our attention to even values of n, we are clearly justified in saying that the sequence

$$\alpha_2, \ \alpha_4,..., \ \alpha_{2n},... \tag{1}$$

converges to α. On the other hand, if all we know is that the sequence (1) converges to α, then we are not justified in saying that $\alpha_n \to \alpha$; we simply have no information about the odd values of n.

Now consider an infinite series

$$a_1+a_2+a_3+a_4+..., \tag{2}$$

and the same series with its terms bracketed

$$(a_1+a_2)+(a_3+a_4)+.... \tag{3}$$

Let $$s_n \equiv a_1+a_2+...+a_n.$$

In thinking of (3) as an infinite series, we consider (a_1+a_2) as one term, (a_3+a_4) as the next, and so on. To find the sum of this series we consider the limit, as $n \to \infty$, of

$$(a_1+a_2)+(a_3+a_4)+... \quad \text{to } n \text{ terms}$$
$$= a_1+...+a_{2n} = s_{2n}.$$

As with the sequence (α_n) above, if we know that $s_n \to s$, then we can at once say that $s_{2n} \to s$: that is to say, if we know that (2) is a convergent series and has a certain sum, then we can at once say that the bracketed series (3) is convergent and has the same sum. But if all we know is that the bracketed series (3) is convergent and has a certain sum, then all our information is limited to s_{2n}, odd values of n are unaccounted for, and we are not justified in saying that the series (2) is convergent until we have investigated the sequence (s_{2n+1}).

In like manner, if $n_1, n_2, n_3,...$ is a sequence of steadily increasing integers, then of the two statements

$$\lim_{r \to \infty} \alpha_r = \alpha, \qquad \lim_{n_r \to \infty} \alpha_{n_r} = \alpha$$

we can deduce the second from the first but not the first from the second. So, in considering series, of the two statements

$$u_1 + u_2 + \ldots \quad \text{is convergent and its sum is } s,$$

$$(u_1 + \ldots + u_{n_1}) + (u_{n_1+1} + \ldots + u_{n_2}) + \ldots$$

$$\text{is convergent and its sum is } s,$$

we can deduce the second from the first but not the first from the second.

Briefly, we may put brackets in and be sure of our results, but if we take brackets out we must subject our work to careful examination.

Examples XIII

1. The series $(1-\frac{1}{2})+(\frac{1}{3}-\frac{1}{4})+\ldots$

has a general term $\dfrac{1}{2n-1} - \dfrac{1}{2n} = \dfrac{1}{2n(2n-1)}$

and is convergent (the terms are comparable with those of $\sum n^{-2}$).

It does not at once follow that

$$1 - \tfrac{1}{2} + \tfrac{1}{3} - \tfrac{1}{4} + \ldots$$

is convergent: all we know from the previous work is that

$$s_{2n} \equiv 1 - \frac{1}{2} + \frac{1}{3} - \frac{1}{4} + \ldots - \frac{1}{2n} \to s.$$

But we can easily complete our work: for

$$s_{2n+1} - s_{2n} = \frac{1}{2n+1} \quad \text{and} \to 0 \text{ as } n \to \infty.$$

But $s_{2n} \to s$, and so $s_{2n+1} = (s_{2n+1} - s_{2n}) + s_{2n} \to 0 + s = s$; hence $s_n \to s$ whether n be odd or even.

2. The series $(2-\frac{3}{2})+(\frac{4}{3}-\frac{5}{4})+\ldots$

is the same as the series in Example 1. But if we remove the brackets, we now get

$$2 - \tfrac{3}{2} + \tfrac{4}{3} - \tfrac{5}{4} + \ldots.$$

We see that

$$s_{2n} = 2 - \frac{3}{2} + \frac{4}{3} - \frac{5}{4} + \ldots - \frac{2n+1}{2n}$$

$$= 1 - \frac{1}{2} + \frac{1}{3} - \frac{1}{4} + \ldots - \frac{1}{2n},$$

$$s_{2n+1} = 2 - \frac{3}{2} + \frac{4}{3} - \frac{5}{4} + \ldots + \frac{2n+2}{2n+1}$$

$$= 1 + 1 - \frac{1}{2} + \frac{1}{3} - \frac{1}{4} + \ldots + \frac{1}{2n+1},$$

$$s_{2n+1} - s_{2n} \to 1.$$

The series without brackets is not convergent.

3. Prove that
$$1+(2-\tfrac{3}{2})+(\tfrac{4}{3}-\tfrac{5}{4})+\ldots = 2-(\tfrac{3}{2}-\tfrac{4}{3})-(\tfrac{5}{4}-\tfrac{6}{5})-\ldots.$$

4. Prove that
$$(1-\tfrac{1}{2})+(\tfrac{1}{3}-\tfrac{1}{4})+\ldots = 1-(\tfrac{1}{2}-\tfrac{1}{3})-(\tfrac{1}{4}-\tfrac{1}{5})-\ldots.$$

2. Change of order of the terms of a series

2.1. In a finite number of terms, say

$$a_1+a_2+\ldots+a_n, \tag{4}$$

the algebraic sum is unaltered by writing the terms in a different order.

In an infinite series we must first say what we mean by 'writing the terms in a different order'.

DEFINITION. *The series*
$$b_1+b_2+b_3+\ldots$$
is the series $a_1+a_2+a_3+\ldots$
with its terms in a different order if every b_r comes somewhere in the a series and every a_r comes somewhere in the b series; $\sum b_n$ is also said to be a rearrangement of $\sum a_n$.

EXAMPLES. (i) $1-\tfrac{1}{2}+\tfrac{1}{3}-\tfrac{1}{4}+\tfrac{1}{5}-\tfrac{1}{6}+\ldots,$
and $-\tfrac{1}{2}+1-\tfrac{1}{4}+\tfrac{1}{3}-\tfrac{1}{6}+\tfrac{1}{5}+\ldots;$
(ii) $1-\tfrac{1}{2}+\tfrac{1}{3}-\tfrac{1}{4}+\tfrac{1}{5}-\tfrac{1}{6}+\ldots,$ (5)
and $1+\tfrac{1}{3}-\tfrac{1}{2}+\tfrac{1}{5}+\tfrac{1}{7}-\tfrac{1}{4}+\ldots.$

The second example brings out a point that marks an important difference between finite and infinite series, namely, we can go on for as long as we like putting two positive terms to one negative term. If we were dealing with a finite number of terms, say 20 terms, some of which were positive and some negative, and began by putting two positive to one negative, we should be obliged to stop when we had exhausted all of one sign and fill in with those terms we had so far left out. For example, the 20 terms
$$1-\tfrac{1}{2}+\tfrac{1}{3}-\tfrac{1}{4}+\ldots+\tfrac{1}{19}-\tfrac{1}{20}$$
may be rearranged as
$$1+\tfrac{1}{3}-\tfrac{1}{2}+\tfrac{1}{5}+\tfrac{1}{7}-\tfrac{1}{4}+\ldots+\tfrac{1}{17}+\tfrac{1}{19}-\tfrac{1}{10}-\tfrac{1}{12}-\tfrac{1}{14}-\tfrac{1}{16}-\tfrac{1}{18}-\tfrac{1}{20}.$$
Here we have gone on as long as possible putting two positives

to one negative, but at the end we have been obliged to redress the balance by putting in all the negatives we had previously left out.

But, as we have seen, when rearranging the infinite series (5) we can continue *ad infinitum* with two positives to one negative. We cannot expect that the sum of the series will remain the same as it was before.

2.2. Suppose that $\quad a_1+a_2+\ldots$
is a given series and that
$$b_1+b_2+\ldots$$
is a rearrangement of it. The sum of the first series is the limit, if it exist, of a sequence
$$s_1, \ s_2,\ldots, \ s_n,\ldots, \quad \text{where } s_n \equiv a_1+\ldots+a_n;$$
the sum of the second series is the limit, if it exist, of a sequence
$$\sigma_1, \ \sigma_2,\ldots, \ \sigma_n,\ldots, \quad \text{where } \sigma_n \equiv b_1+\ldots+b_n.$$

The two sequences may well be quite dissimilar and it is, on the face of it, as likely as not that their limits will be different.

There is one important general theorem that deals with rearrangements of infinite series, namely,

THEOREM 26. *If a series is absolutely convergent, then its sum is unaffected by any change in the order of its terms.*

2.3. Proof of Theorem 26 for a series of positive terms.
We first prove the theorem for a series of positive terms. Let each u_n be positive, and let
$$v_1+v_2+\ldots+v_n+\ldots$$
be a rearrangement of the series
$$u_1+u_2+\ldots+u_n+\ldots.$$

As yet, we make no assumption that either series is convergent.

Let $\quad s_n \equiv u_1+\ldots+u_n, \quad \sigma_n \equiv v_1+\ldots+v_n.$

For any definite value of n, s_n contains n terms each of which comes, sooner or later, in the v series, and so we can find a corresponding m such that σ_m contains all the terms of s_n (and possibly others not contained in s_n). Since each term is positive, $\sigma_m \geqslant s_n$. Hence

given n, $\exists$ a corresponding m . $\sigma_m \geqslant s_n$.

Suppose now that the v series is convergent. Then the sequence (σ_n) has a finite upper bound σ, say. Since $\sigma_m \geqslant s_n$,

$$\sigma \geqslant \sigma_m \geqslant s_n.$$

Hence the upper bound (cf. the definition of Chap. III, § 1.2) of the sequence (s_n), say s, cannot exceed σ: hence the u series is convergent and

$$\sigma \geqslant s. \tag{6}$$

But, for any definite value of n, σ_n contains n terms each of which comes, sooner or later, in the u series, and so we can find a corresponding M such that s_M contains all the terms of σ_n (and possibly others not contained in σ_n). Since each term is positive,

$$s_M \geqslant \sigma_n.$$

Since $s \geqslant s_M$, it follows that $s \geqslant \sigma_n$, and so σ, the upper bound of the σ_n, cannot exceed s: hence

$$s \geqslant \sigma. \tag{7}$$

By (6) and (7), $s = \sigma$,

and the u series has the same sum as the v series.

Suppose now that the v series is divergent. Then σ_n increases indefinitely and, since we can find an s_M to exceed any given σ_n, s_n must also increase indefinitely and hence the u series is also divergent.

Alternative treatment of divergence. Suppose the v series is divergent. Then

$$A > 0; \quad \exists\, N \; . \; \sigma_n > A \quad \text{when } n \geqslant N.$$

But, as we have seen, $\exists\, M$. $s_M \geqslant \sigma_N$ and hence

$$\exists\, M \; . \; s_m > A \quad \text{when } m \geqslant M.$$

Hence the u series is also divergent.

2.4. Proof of Theorem 26 for absolutely convergent series. Let $\sum a_n$ be an absolutely convergent series; let P be the sum of its positive terms alone, Q the sum of its negative terms alone. Then (Theorem 23) if s is the sum of $\sum a_n$,

$$s = P + Q \quad (Q \text{ is, of course, negative}).$$

Any change in the order of the terms of $\sum a_n$ gives a new series which, by §2.3, is such that

its positive terms alone converge to P,

its negative terms alone converge to Q.

Hence (Theorem 23) the new series is absolutely convergent and its sum is $P+Q$, so that the new series has the same sum as the old one.

EXAMPLE. The two series

$$1-\frac{1}{2^2}+\frac{1}{3^2}-\frac{1}{4^2}+\cdots, \qquad 1+\frac{1}{3^2}-\frac{1}{2^2}+\frac{1}{5^2}+\frac{1}{7^2}-\frac{1}{4^2}+\cdots$$

are absolutely convergent and have the same sum. This should be contrasted with the example given in §2.5.

2.5. Further results about rearrangements of series. If we rearrange the order of the terms of *a non-absolutely convergent series* $\sum a_n$, we may or may not change the sum of the series. Roughly speaking, the sum will be changed if we interfere too much with the balance between positive and negative terms.

In the following example the new series gives more weight to the positive terms than the original series does.

EXAMPLE. The series

$$1-\tfrac{1}{2}+\tfrac{1}{3}-\tfrac{1}{4}+\cdots, \tag{8}$$

$$1+\tfrac{1}{3}-\tfrac{1}{2}+\tfrac{1}{5}+\tfrac{1}{7}-\tfrac{1}{4}+\cdots \tag{9}$$

are convergent and their sums are $\log 2$, $\tfrac{3}{2}\log 2$ respectively.

For the purpose of working this example we assume the result, which will be proved in Chapter XIV, that as $n \to \infty$,

$$1+\frac{1}{2}+\frac{1}{3}+\cdots+\frac{1}{n}-\log n \to \gamma,$$

where γ is a constant (Euler's constant).

Assuming this result, we see that we may write

$$1+\frac{1}{2}+\frac{1}{3}+\cdots+\frac{1}{n} = \log n+\gamma_n,$$

where $\gamma_n \to \gamma$ as $n \to \infty$. (This procedure reduces the difficulty of handling limit problems connected with $1+\tfrac{1}{2}+\tfrac{1}{3}+\cdots$.)

The series (8) is an alternating series whose terms tend

steadily to zero and so (Theorem 18) the series is convergent. Let s_n denote the algebraic sum of its first n terms; s the sum of the series. Then

$$s = \lim_{n\to\infty} s_n = \lim_{n\to\infty} s_{2n} = \lim_{n\to\infty}\left(1-\frac{1}{2}+\dots-\frac{1}{2n}\right)$$

$$= \lim_{n\to\infty}\left[\left(1+\frac{1}{2}+\frac{1}{3}+\dots+\frac{1}{2n}\right)-2\left(\frac{1}{2}+\frac{1}{4}+\dots+\frac{1}{2n}\right)\right]$$

$$= \lim_{n\to\infty}\left[\left(1+\frac{1}{2}+\frac{1}{3}+\dots+\frac{1}{2n}\right)-\left(1+\frac{1}{2}+\dots+\frac{1}{n}\right)\right]$$

$$= \lim_{n\to\infty} (\log 2n+\gamma_{2n}-\log n-\gamma_n)$$

$$= \lim_{n\to\infty} (\log 2+\gamma_{2n}-\gamma_n)$$

$$= \log 2,$$

since $\gamma_{2n}-\gamma_n \to \gamma-\gamma = 0$.

The series (9) is not obviously convergent by any of the standard tests. We begin by considering the sum of $3n$ terms (equivalent to first considering the series where the terms are bracketed in groups of three). Let σ_n denote the sum of the first n terms of (9). Then

$$\sigma_{3n} = \left(1+\frac{1}{3}-\frac{1}{2}\right)+\left(\frac{1}{5}+\frac{1}{7}-\frac{1}{4}\right)+\dots+\left(\frac{1}{4n-3}+\frac{1}{4n-1}-\frac{1}{2n}\right)$$

$$= \left(1+\frac{1}{3}+\frac{1}{5}+\dots+\frac{1}{4n-1}\right)-\frac{1}{2}\left(1+\frac{1}{2}+\dots+\frac{1}{n}\right)$$

$$= \left(1+\frac{1}{2}+\frac{1}{3}+\dots+\frac{1}{4n}\right)-\frac{1}{2}\left(1+\frac{1}{2}+\dots+\frac{1}{2n}\right)-$$

$$-\frac{1}{2}\left(1+\frac{1}{2}+\dots+\frac{1}{n}\right)$$

$$= \log 4n+\gamma_{4n}-\tfrac{1}{2}(\log 2n+\gamma_{2n})-\tfrac{1}{2}(\log n+\gamma_n)$$

$$= \tfrac{3}{2}\log 2+(1-\tfrac{1}{2}-\tfrac{1}{2})\log n+\gamma_{4n}-\tfrac{1}{2}\gamma_{2n}-\tfrac{1}{2}\gamma_n \to \tfrac{3}{2}\log 2.$$

Further

$$\sigma_{3n+1} = \sigma_{3n}+\frac{1}{4n+1} \to \frac{3}{2}\log 2,$$

$$\sigma_{3n+2} = \sigma_{3n}+\frac{1}{4n+1}+\frac{1}{4n+3} \to \frac{3}{2}\log 2.$$

Hence, not only the bracketed series

$$(1+\tfrac{1}{3}-\tfrac{1}{2})+(\tfrac{1}{5}+\tfrac{1}{7}-\tfrac{1}{4})+...,$$

but also the series, without brackets,

$$1+\tfrac{1}{3}-\tfrac{1}{2}+\tfrac{1}{5}+\tfrac{1}{7}-\tfrac{1}{4}+...,$$

is convergent and has the sum $\tfrac{3}{2}\log 2$.

3. The multiplication of two infinite series

3.1. Suppose, for a moment, that we disregard all questions of convergence and see what form of answer we should get if we were to multiply together

$$a_1+a_2 x+a_3 x^2+...+a_n x^{n-1}+...$$

and $\qquad b_1+b_2 x+b_3 x^2+...+b_n x^{n-1}+... .$

The form of answer is, clearly,

$$a_1 b_1+(a_1 b_2+a_2 b_1)x+...+(a_1 b_n+a_2 b_{n-1}+...+a_n b_1)x^{n-1}+... .$$

We state our theorems about the multiplication of series in such a form that they can be used easily for power series. The coefficient of x^{n-1} in the previous work gives the reason for our choice of c_n in the subsequent work.

3.2. THEOREM 27. *If* $\sum a_n$, $\sum b_n$ *converge absolutely, and*

$$c_n = a_n b_1+a_{n-1}b_2+...+a_1 b_n,$$

then $\sum c_n$ *is absolutely convergent and* $\sum c_n = (\sum a_n)(\sum b_n)$.

Let

$$A_n = a_1+a_2+...+a_n, \qquad A'_n = |a_1|+|a_2|+...+|a_n|,$$
$$B_n = b_1+b_2+...+b_n, \qquad B'_n = |b_1|+|b_2|+...+|b_n|,$$

and let $A_n \to A$, $B_n \to B$, $A'_n \to A'$, $B'_n \to B'$.

Write down the terms of the product $A_n B_n$ thus:

$$
\begin{array}{ccccccc}
a_1 b_1 & a_1 b_2 & a_1 b_3 & . & . & . & a_1 b_n \\
a_2 b_1 & a_2 b_2 & a_2 b_3 & . & . & . & a_2 b_n \\
a_3 b_1 & a_3 b_2 & a_3 b_3 & . & . & . & a_3 b_n \\
. & . & . & . & . & . & . \\
a_n b_1 & a_n b_2 & a_n b_3 & . & . & . & a_n b_n .
\end{array}
\qquad \text{(S)}
$$

Consider $A_n B_n$ set out in the form

$$A_1 B_1 + (A_2 B_2 - A_1 B_1) +$$
$$+ (A_3 B_3 - A_2 B_2) + \dots + (A_n B_n - A_{n-1} B_{n-1}),$$

that is, $\quad a_1 b_1 + (a_2 b_1 + a_2 b_2 + a_1 b_2) + \dots \quad$ to n terms. $\qquad$ (1)

Now remove the brackets from (1) and consider the infinite series

$$a_1 b_1 + a_2 b_1 + a_2 b_2 + a_1 b_2 + a_3 b_1 + a_3 b_2 + \dots . \qquad (2)$$

First step. The sum of the moduli of any number, say m, of its terms $<$ some $A_n' B_n'$; for we can choose n big enough to ensure that all the m terms are in the square (S) and the sum of the moduli of all the terms in (S) is $A_n' B_n'$.

But A_n' is a m.i. sequence and so $A_n' < A'$ and, similarly, $B_n' < B'$. Hence $A_n' B_n' < A'B'$. Hence (Theorem 6) the series formed by taking the absolute values of the terms in (2) is convergent; that is, (2) is absolutely convergent.

Second step. The sum of the series (2), which has no brackets, is equal to the sum of the series, with brackets,

$$a_1 b_1 + (a_2 b_1 + a_2 b_2 + a_1 b_2) + \dots + (a_n b_1 + a_n b_2 + \dots + a_1 b_n) + \dots$$
$$= \lim_{n \to \infty} A_n B_n,$$

as we see by looking at (1), which is another way of writing $A_n B_n$. But $A_n \to A$, $B_n \to B$. Hence (2) has the sum AB.

Third step. Since (2) is absolutely convergent, any series got from it by rearranging its terms is also absolutely convergent and has the same sum. Hence

$$a_1 b_1 + a_2 b_1 + a_1 b_2 + a_3 b_1 + a_2 b_2 + a_1 b_3 + a_4 b_1 + \dots \qquad (3)$$

is absolutely convergent and has the sum AB.

Finally, the series got by putting brackets in (3), namely,

$$a_1 b_1 + (a_2 b_1 + a_1 b_2) + \dots + (a_n b_1 + a_{n-1} b_2 + \dots + a_1 b_n) + \dots, \qquad (4)$$

i.e. $\qquad\qquad c_1 + c_2 + \dots + c_n + \dots,$

is absolutely convergent and has the sum AB.

EXAMPLES XIV

Questions 1–6 may be made to depend on the fact that

$$1 + \frac{1}{2} + \frac{1}{3} + \dots + \frac{1}{n} - \log n \to \gamma \quad \text{as } n \to \infty.$$

1. $1 + \dfrac{1}{3} + \dfrac{1}{5} + \dots + \dfrac{1}{2n+1} - \dfrac{1}{2} \log n \to \dfrac{1}{2}\gamma + \log 2.$

2. $1+\dfrac{1}{2}-\dfrac{1}{3}+\dfrac{1}{4}+\dfrac{1}{5}-\dfrac{1}{6}+...+\dfrac{1}{3n-1}-\dfrac{1}{3n}-\dfrac{1}{3}\log n \to \dfrac{1}{3}\gamma+\log 3.$

3. $1-\tfrac{1}{2}+\tfrac{1}{3}-\tfrac{1}{4}+...$ is convergent: its sum is $\log 2$.

4. $\displaystyle\sum_{n=1}^{\infty}\frac{1}{n(16n^2-1)} = -2+3\log 2.$

5. The series obtained by rearranging the series

$$1-\tfrac{1}{2}+\tfrac{1}{3}-\tfrac{1}{4}+...$$

so that 3 positives alternate with 2 negatives, that is,

$$1+\tfrac{1}{3}+\tfrac{1}{5}-\tfrac{1}{2}-\tfrac{1}{4}+\tfrac{1}{7}+...,$$

has the sum $\tfrac{1}{2}\log 6$.

6. If, in Example 5, p positives alternate with q negatives, the sum is $\log 2 + \tfrac{1}{2}\log(p/q)$.

7. If
$$A(x) = a_0+a_1 x+a_2 x^2+..., \qquad B(x) = b_0+b_1 x+b_2 x^2+...,$$
each series being absolutely convergent, and if
$$c_n = a_n b_0+a_{n-1} b_1+...+a_0 b_n,$$
then $A(x)B(x) = c_0+c_1 x+c_2 x^2+...$.

8. If $a_0+a_1 x+...+a_n x^n+...$ is absolutely convergent when $|x| < 1$, and if $A(x)$ is its sum, prove that, when $|x| < 1$,

$$(1-x)^{-1}A(x) = \sum_{n=0}^{\infty} s_n x^n,$$

where $s_n = a_0+a_1+...+a_n$.

9. Prove that, if $A_n^r \equiv \dfrac{(n+r)!}{n!\,r!}$ and $A_0^r \equiv 1$, then

$$\sum_{\nu=0}^{n} A_\nu^r = A_n^{r+1}.$$

HINT. One method is to write

$$\sum_{\nu=0}^{n} A_\nu^r = A_n^r\Big\{1+\frac{n}{n+r}+\frac{n(n-1)}{(n+r)(n+r-1)}+...\Big\}$$

and to use (cf. Misc. Exx. on Chaps. I–VII) the fact that

$$\frac{n+r+1}{r+1} = 1+\frac{n}{n+r}\cdot\frac{n+r}{r+1} = 1+\frac{n}{n+r}\Big\{1+\frac{n-1}{n+r-1}\cdot\frac{n+r-1}{r+1}\Big\}.\text{ etc.}$$

10. Prove, by induction (using Example 9), that when $|x| < 1$

$$(1-x)^{-r-1} = \sum_{n=0}^{\infty} A_n^r x^n.$$

11. By writing $(1-x)^{-r-s-2} = (1-x)^{-r-1}(1-x)^{-s-1}$, prove that

$$\sum_{\nu=0}^{n} A_\nu^r A_{n-\nu}^s = A_n^{r+s+1}.$$

12. Prove that the series

$$1 + x + \frac{x^2}{2!} + \frac{x^3}{3!} + \cdots$$

is absolutely convergent for all real values of x. If $E(x)$ denotes its sum, prove that $E(x)E(y) = E(x+y)$. (Prove the result by means of Theorem 27, not by quoting $e^x \cdot e^y = e^{x+y}$.)

4. Abel's continuity theorem†

4.1. Before we obtain the next theorem about the multiplication of infinite series we establish two preliminary theorems about power series, a topic we shall not discuss systematically until later.

THEOREM 28. *If $\sum a_n$ is convergent (not necessarily absolutely convergent), then $\sum a_n x^n$ is absolutely convergent when $|x| < 1$.*

Since $\sum a_n$ is convergent, $a_n \to 0$. Hence

$$\exists \ N \ . \ |a_n| < \tfrac{1}{2} \quad \text{when } n \geqslant N.$$

When $|x| < 1$, $\sum |x|^n$ is convergent. By the comparison test,

$$\sum_{N}^{\infty} |a_n x^n|$$

is therefore convergent when $|x| < 1$. Hence (Theorem 13) $\sum_{n=0}^{\infty} a_n x^n$ is absolutely convergent when $|x| < 1$.

4.2. In the enunciation of our next theorem we employ the idea of a function of x tending to a definite limit as x tends to a definite value. The formal definitions are

DEFINITION. FORM B. *A function $f(x)$ is said to tend to the limit l as x tends to a certain value a from values less than a if, having chosen any positive number ϵ whatsoever, we can then find an X such that*

$$|f(x) - l| < \epsilon \quad \text{when } X < x < a.$$

We write $\quad f(x) \to l \quad as \ x \to a - 0.$

Notice that we are completely uninterested in what the value of $f(a)$ may be: we want the behaviour of $f(x)$ for values of x a little less than a.

---

† Some readers will prefer to omit all save the result of Theorem 30 on a first reading.

DEFINITION. FORM C. *A function $f(x)$ is said to tend to the limit l as x tends to a certain value a from values less than a, if*

$$\epsilon > 0; \quad \exists \ X \ . \ |f(x)-l| < \epsilon \quad when \ X < x < a.$$

We shall use, without the formality of a separate proof, theorems analogous to those given in Chapter VI, § 1.1.

There is a similar definition dealing with values of x greater than a.

DEFINITION. *$f(x) \to l$ as $x \to a$ from values greater than a if*

$$\epsilon > 0; \quad \exists \ X \ . \ |f(x)-l| < \epsilon \quad when \ X > x > a.$$

We write $\qquad f(x) \to l \quad as \ x \to a+0.$

Finally, if $f(x) \to l$ both as $x \to a-0$ and as $x \to a+0$, then we say that $f(x) \to l$ as $x \to a$.

THEOREM 29.† *If $\sum\limits_{n=0}^{\infty} a_n$ is convergent and s is its sum, and if $f(x)$ denotes the sum of $\sum\limits_{n=0}^{\infty} a_n x^n$ when $|x| < 1$ (cf. Theorem 28), then $f(x) \to s$ as $x \to 1$ from values less than 1.*

Let $s_n \equiv a_0 + a_1 + ... + a_n$. Then, since $s_n \to s$, two facts may be stated about s_n. First, by Theorem 1,

$$\exists \ K \ . \ |s_n| < K \quad \text{for all } n,$$

so that (Theorem 2) $|s| \leqslant K$, and

$$|s-s_n| \leqslant |s| + |s_n| < 2K \quad \text{for all } n. \tag{1}$$

Next, on using the device introduced in Chapter VI, § 2,

$$\epsilon, k > 0; \quad \exists \ N \ . \ |s-s_n| < \epsilon k \quad \text{when } n \geqslant N. \tag{2}$$

We now consider $\qquad \dfrac{f(x)-s}{1-x}.$

When $|x| < 1$, we have

$$f(x) = a_0 + a_1 x + a_2 x^2 + ... + a_n x^n + ...,$$
$$(1-x)^{-1} = 1 + x + x^2 + ... + x^n + ...,$$

the two series being absolutely convergent. Hence, by Theorem 27, we may multiply them, collecting like powers of x, and so obtain

$$(1-x)^{-1}f(x) = a_0 + (a_0+a_1)x + (a_0+a_1+a_2)x^2 + ...$$
$$= s_0 + s_1 x + s_2 x^2 + ... + s_n x^n + ...$$

† For an alternative proof see Examples XVI, 8.

Hence, when $0 < x < 1$,

$$\frac{f(x)-s}{1-x} = (s_0-s)+(s_1-s)x+\ldots+(s_n-s)x^n+\ldots, \qquad (3)$$

and so, by (1) and (2), and by the use of Theorem 8,

$$\left|\frac{f(x)-s}{1-x}\right| < 2K(1+x+\ldots+x^{N-1})+\epsilon k(x^N+x^{N+1}+\ldots)$$
$$= 2K\frac{1-x^N}{1-x}+\epsilon k\frac{x^N}{1-x}.$$

Accordingly, when $0 < x < 1$,

$$|f(x)-s| < 2K(1-x^N)+\epsilon k. \qquad (4)$$

But, N being fixed, as also are ϵ and k,

$$\exists\ X\ .\ 1-x^N < \epsilon k \quad \text{when } X < x < 1.$$

In (2) take $k = 1/(2K+1)$. We then see that

$$\epsilon > 0;\ \exists\ X\ .\ |f(x)-s| < \epsilon \quad \text{when } X < x < 1,$$

that is, $\qquad\qquad f(x) \to s \quad \text{as } x \to 1-0.$

4.3. The reader will see that the proof in 4.2 consists of writing down (3)—which is simple algebra apart from the use of Theorem 27—getting an $\epsilon k/(1-x)$ out of (2) for $n \geqslant N$ and getting a multiple of ϵk for the terms not so dealt with by taking x sufficiently near to 1.

5. Multiplication of series (*continued*)

THEOREM 30. *If c_n is defined as*

$$a_1 b_n+a_2 b_{n-1}+\ldots+a_n b_1,$$

then $\left(\sum\limits_{n=1}^{\infty} a_n\right)\left(\sum\limits_{n=1}^{\infty} b_n\right) = \sum\limits_{n=1}^{\infty} c_n$ *whenever all three series are convergent.*

Let each of the series $\sum a_n$, $\sum b_n$, $\sum c_n$ be convergent; let their sums be A, B, C. Then the series

$$\sum_{n=1}^{\infty} a_n x^{n-1}, \qquad \sum_{n=1}^{\infty} b_n x^{n-1}$$

are absolutely convergent (Theorem 28) when $0 < x < 1$, and their product (Theorem 27) is then

$$\sum_{n=1}^{\infty} c_n x^{n-1}.$$

But, by Theorem 29, $\sum a_n x^{n-1} \to A$, $\sum b_n x^{n-1} \to B$, and $\sum c_n x^{n-1} \to C$ as $x \to 1-0$. Hence, by the analogue of Chapter VI, §1.1, $AB = C$.

EXAMPLES XV

1. Prove that

$$\frac{1}{2}\left(x - \frac{1}{2}x^2 + \frac{1}{3}x^3 - \ldots\right)^2 = \sum_{n=2}^{\infty} (-1)^n \left(1 + \frac{1}{2} + \ldots + \frac{1}{n-1}\right)\frac{x^n}{n}$$

(a) when $|x| < 1$, (b) when $x = 1$.

$\left[\text{Assume in } (b) \text{ that } \dfrac{1}{n+1}\left(1 + \dfrac{1}{2} + \ldots + \dfrac{1}{n}\right) \to 0.\right]$

2. Assuming the expansion

$$\tan^{-1}x = x - \tfrac{1}{3}x^3 + \tfrac{1}{5}x^5 - \ldots,$$

prove that

$$\tfrac{1}{2}(\tan^{-1}x)^2 = \sum_{n=0}^{\infty} (-1)^n \frac{x^{2n+2}}{2n+2}\left(1 + \frac{1}{3} + \ldots + \frac{1}{2n+1}\right).$$

Prove that the series are absolutely convergent when $|x| < 1$ and are convergent when $x = 1$.

3. By first putting $x = -y$ in Examples XIV, 10, show that

$$2^{-r-1} = \sum_{n=0}^{\infty} (-1)^n A_n^r$$

when r is a positive integer.

4. Prove that each of the series

$$x - \tfrac{1}{2}x^2 + \tfrac{1}{3}x^3 - \tfrac{1}{4}x^4 + \ldots,$$
$$x - \tfrac{1}{3}x^3 + \tfrac{1}{5}x^5 - \ldots$$

is absolutely convergent when $|x| < 1$ and that the functions they represent tend to the sums of the series

$$1 - \tfrac{1}{2} + \tfrac{1}{3} - \tfrac{1}{4} + \ldots,$$
$$1 - \tfrac{1}{3} + \tfrac{1}{5} - \ldots$$

as x tends to 1 from values less than 1.

5. Consider the validity of $(\sum a_n)(\sum b_n) = \sum c_n$, where

$$c_n = a_1 b_n + a_2 b_{n-1} + \ldots + a_n b_1,$$

in the three cases

(i) $a_n = b_n = n^{-2}$,   (ii) $a_n = b_n = (-1)^n n^{-1}$,

(iii) $a_n = b_n = (-1)^n n^{-1/2}$.

CHAPTER XI

UNIFORM CONVERGENCE

FOREWORD. This chapter is rather long. The reader may find the following plan useful on a first reading. Master §§ 1, 2; get a first, rough idea of the theorems in §§ 3, 4, 5; see how these theorems apply to some of the examples at the end of the chapter; make a more careful study of §§ 3, 4, 5. Theorems 36, 37 should be omitted on a first reading.

1. Preliminary discussion

We have proved that we can add and subtract (Chap. VI, § 3) convergent series, and that we can multiply them together when certain conditions are satisfied (Chap. X). We now start on the problem 'When can we integrate and differentiate infinite series?'

Suppose we know that, for each and every x such that $a \leqslant x \leqslant b$, the sequence

$$\alpha_n(x) \quad (n = 1, 2, 3, \ldots)$$

tends to a limit. This limit depends upon x; let it be denoted by $\alpha(x)$. Then what we know is this: **if we first fix x,** then

$$\epsilon > 0; \quad \exists \ N \ . \ |\alpha(x) - \alpha_n(x)| < \epsilon \quad \text{when } n \geqslant N. \tag{1}$$

If we move to another x and keep the same ϵ, then the statement

$$|\alpha(x) - \alpha_n(x)| < \epsilon \quad \text{when } n \geqslant N$$

may cease to be true if we keep the same N: we may need to take a larger N for the statement to be true. This possibility that N will grow bigger and bigger as we move to different x will lead to difficulty in many problems. So, to cut out all such difficulty, we consider a different type of convergence, namely, *uniform convergence in an interval* (a, b). We say that $\alpha_n(x)$ converges uniformly in the interval (a, b) to the limit $\alpha(x)$ if

$$\epsilon > 0; \quad \exists \ N \ . \ |\alpha(x) - \alpha_n(x)| < \epsilon \quad \text{when } n \geqslant N \text{ and } a \leqslant x \leqslant b. \tag{2}$$

In (2) there is no question of first fixing x; we fix the interval (a, b) and not any special x in it, and then (2) says 'If we put down any positive number ϵ whatsoever, there is some number N such that $|\alpha(x) - \alpha_n(x)| < \epsilon$ when $n \geqslant N$, no matter what x of $a \leqslant x \leqslant b$ we consider'.

2. Formal definitions

2.1. It will be convenient to make precise the meaning of 'interval'. Geometrically, an interval on a straight line consists of all points lying between two fixed points, the ends of the interval: sometimes we want to think of the end-points as belonging to the interval (a closed interval), sometimes we want to exclude the end-points from our consideration (an open interval). Analytically, the definitions are

The closed interval (a, b) consists of all numbers x such that $a \leqslant x \leqslant b$. The open† interval $)a, b($ consists of all numbers x such that $a < x < b$.

In this book 'interval' will mean 'closed interval' unless the contrary is stated. The phrase 'all x in (a, b)' will mean 'all numbers x such that $a \leqslant x \leqslant b$'.

Uniform convergence can be defined with respect to a closed interval, an open interval, or indeed with respect to any set of values of the variable x. But we shall, for simplicity, confine our attention to closed intervals.

Definition of uniform convergence in an interval. *The sequence $\alpha_n(x)$ is said to converge uniformly to the limit $\alpha(x)$ in the interval (a, b) if*

$\epsilon > 0;\ \exists\ N$ **. for all x in (a, b),** $|\alpha(x) - \alpha_n(x)| < \epsilon$ *when $n \geqslant N$.*

A less emphatic form of the last line is

$\epsilon > 0;\ \exists\ N$ **.** $|\alpha(x) - \alpha_n(x)| < \epsilon$ when $n \geqslant N$ and $a \leqslant x \leqslant b$.

The reader may use either so long as he holds firmly to the fact that ϵ having been set down, it is possible to find an N that governs the whole interval.

The series $\quad u_1(x) + u_2(x) + ... + u_n(x) + ...$

is said to converge uniformly to the sum $s(x)$ in the interval (a, b) if, with $s_n(x) \equiv u_1(x) + ... + u_n(x)$,

$\epsilon > 0;\ \exists\ N$ **. for all x in (a, b),** $|s(x) - s_n(x)| < \epsilon$ *when $n \geqslant N$.*

That is, the sequence $s_n(x)$ converges uniformly to $s(x)$ in (a, b).

† The brackets open outwards to denote an open interval.

2.2. An example. Consider the sequence

$$x^n \quad (n = 1, 2, 3,...)$$

when $0 < x < 1$. If we fix x, then $x^n \to 0$ as $n \to \infty$. If we fix a definite number δ, as near 1 as we please but less than it, then

$$x^n \leqslant \delta^n \quad \text{when } 0 \leqslant x \leqslant \delta.$$

Since $\delta^n \to 0$ as $n \to \infty$,

$$\epsilon > 0; \quad \exists \; N \; . \; \delta^n < \epsilon \quad \text{when } n \geqslant N,$$

and so $\exists \; N$. for all x in $(0, \delta)$, $|x^n| < \epsilon$ when $n \geqslant N$. That is to say, the sequence (x^n) converges uniformly in $(0, \delta)$ to the limit zero.

The reader will see for himself that the argument breaks down completely if $\delta = 1$: there is not uniform convergence in $(0, 1)$, though there is in any $(0, \delta)$ where $0 < \delta < 1$.

3. Properties of uniformly convergent series

3.1. Integration. THEOREM 31. *If the series*

$$u_1(x) + u_2(x) + ... + u_n(x) + ... \tag{1}$$

converges uniformly to the sum $s(x)$ in the interval (a, b), then

$$\int_a^b s(x) \, dx = \sum_{n=1}^{\infty} \int_a^b u_n(x) \, dx \tag{2}$$

provided $s(x)$ and each $u_n(x)$ can be integrated over (a, b).

The process of forming the R.H.S. of (2) is usually called integrating the series (1) term by term; the theorem itself may be expressed in the form '*A uniformly convergent series may be integrated term by term over a finite range.*'

Consider the graphs

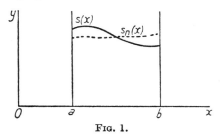

FIG. 1.

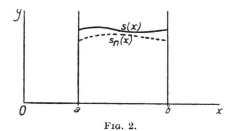

FIG. 2.

wherein the curves $y = s(x)$, $y = s_n(x)$ are shown in typical relative positions: $s_n(x) = u_1(x) + \ldots + u_n(x)$.

Since the series converges uniformly to the sum $s(x)$ in (a, b),

$$\epsilon > 0; \quad \exists\, N \;.\; \text{for all } x \text{ in } (a, b),$$

$$|s(x) - s_n(x)| < \frac{\epsilon}{b-a} \quad \text{when } n \geqslant N.$$

That is, the vertical distance between the two graphs is less than $\epsilon/(b-a)$ at every point, and so the area between the two graphs is less than ϵ. Hence, if $n \geqslant N$, then

$$\left| \int_a^b s(x)\, dx - \int_a^b s_n(x)\, dx \right|,$$

which is less than (Fig. 1) or equal to (Fig. 2) the area between the graphs of $y = s(x)$ and $y = s_n(x)$, is less than ϵ. Hence

$$\epsilon > 0; \quad \exists\, N \;.\; \left| \int_a^b s(x)\, dx - \sum_{r=1}^n \int_a^b u_r(x)\, dx \right| < \epsilon \quad \text{when } n \geqslant N,$$

that is, the series of integrals converges to the integral of $s(x)$.

For readers whose knowledge of integral calculus is sufficiently advanced the following proof is given.

By hypothesis,

$\epsilon, k > 0; \quad \exists\, N \;.\; |s(x) - s_n(x)| < \epsilon k \quad \text{when } n \geqslant N \quad \text{and} \quad a \leqslant x \leqslant b.$

When $n \geqslant N$

$$\left| \int_a^b s(x)\, dx - \int_a^b s_n(x)\, dx \right| = \left| \int_a^b \{s(x) - s_n(x)\}\, dx \right|$$

$$\leqslant \int_a^b |s(x) - s_n(x)|\, dx \leqslant (b-a)k\epsilon.$$

(The modulus of the integral of $f(x) \leqslant$ the integral of $|f(x)|$.)

Take $k = 1/(b-a)$, and we have

$$\epsilon > 0; \quad \exists \; N \; . \; \left| \int\limits_a^b s(x)\,dx - \int\limits_a^b s_n(x)\,dx \right| < \epsilon \quad \text{when } n \geqslant N,$$

and so the series of integrals converges to the integral of $s(x)$.

3.2. Continuity. *A function $f(x)$ is said to be continuous at $x = x_0$ if*

$$\epsilon > 0; \quad \exists \; \delta \; . \; |f(x)-f(x_0)| < \epsilon \quad \text{when } |x-x_0| < \delta.$$

That is to say, given ϵ, there is a δ such that $f(x)$ is within ϵ of $f(x_0)$ whenever x is within δ of x_0; or, again, on using the notation of Chapter X, §4.2, $f(x) \to f(x_0)$ as $x \to x_0$.

We shall make only occasional use of continuity, but it is impossible to give clear enunciations and proofs of some theorems without using it. We shall assume, without proof, that if $f(x)$ is continuous at every x_0 in (a,b), then $f(x)$ can be integrated over the whole or any part of (a,b), and, if

$$F(x) = \int\limits_a^x f(t)\,dt \qquad (a < x < b),$$

then $F'(x) = f(x)$. We assume also (what can be proved as an exercise) that the sum of a finite number of continuous functions is itself a continuous function.

THEOREM 32. *If each $u_n(x)$ is continuous in (a,b) [that is, continuous at each x_0 in (a,b)] and $\sum u_n(x)$ converges uniformly to a sum $s(x)$ in (a,b), then $s(x)$ is continuous in $)a,b($; also*

$$s(x) \to s(a) \text{ as } x \to a+0, \text{ and } s(x) \to s(b) \text{ as } x \to b-0.$$

Let x_0 be any given x in (a,b). By hypothesis,

$$\epsilon, k > 0; \quad \exists \; N \; . \; |s(x)-s_N(x)| < \epsilon k \quad \text{when } a \leqslant x \leqslant b.$$

Hence, for any x in (a,b) other than x_0,

$$|s(x)-s(x_0)| \leqslant |s(x)-s_N(x)| + |s_N(x)-s_N(x_0)| + |s_N(x_0)-s(x_0)|$$
$$< 2\epsilon k + |s_N(x)-s_N(x_0)|.$$

But N is a definite, finite number and so, by hypothesis, $s_N(x)$ is continuous in (a,b). Hence

$$\exists \; \delta \; . \; |s_N(x)-s_N(x_0)| < \epsilon k \quad \text{when } |x-x_0| < \delta.$$

Hence, on taking $k = \frac{1}{3}$,

$$\epsilon > 0; \quad \exists \; \delta \; . \; |s(x)-s(x_0)| < \epsilon \quad \text{when } |x-x_0| < \delta.$$

3.21. *Problem.* In the proof of Theorem 32 we have used nearly the full force, but not quite the full force, of our hypothesis that $\sum u_n(x)$ converges uniformly to the sum $s(x)$. What have we found it unnecessary to use?

3.3. Differentiation. THEOREM 33. *If $\sum u_n(x)$ converges for all x in (a, b), and if each $u_n(x)$ has a continuous differential coefficient in (a, b), then*

$$\frac{d}{dx}\{\sum u_n(x)\} = \sum u'_n(x) \quad (a < x < b),$$

provided THE SERIES OF DIFFERENTIAL COEFFICIENTS *is uniformly convergent.*

Let $\sum u'_n(x) = G(x)$ and $\sum u_n(x) = F(x)$. By Theorem 32, $G(x)$ is continuous and so, if $a < x < b$,

$$\frac{d}{dx}\int_a^x G(t)\,dt = G(x). \tag{1}$$

By Theorem 31, since $\sum u'_n(t)$ converges uniformly in (a, x),

$$\int_a^x G(t)\,dt = \sum \int_a^x u'_n(t)\,dt$$
$$= \sum \{u_n(x) - u_n(a)\}$$
$$= F(x) - F(a)$$

(by the subtraction of two convergent series).

By (1), $\qquad \dfrac{d}{dx}\{F(x)\} = G(x).$

3.4. General Note on Theorems 31, 33. The conditions we have given are *sufficient* to prove the theorems. It is not *necessary* that a series should be uniformly convergent for term-by-term integration to be valid: nor is a continuous differential coefficient necessary to the truth of Theorem 33. We have confined ourselves to the simplest and most common circumstances.

The following examples, taken from Bromwich, *Theory of Infinite Series*, illustrate the fact that not all series can be integrated or differentiated term by term.

EXAMPLE 1. For the sequence

$$s_n(x) = nxe^{-nx^2} \quad (n = 1, 2, 3, ...),$$

$s(x) =$ limit of $s_n(x)$ when $n \to \infty$, x being fixed, $= 0$. The graphs of $y = s_n(x)$ have the general form shown:

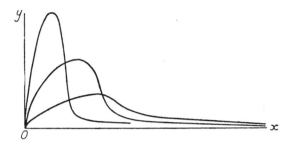

the larger n is, the steeper and the closer to the y-axis is the ascent. The top of the peak is at a height $\sqrt{(\tfrac{1}{2}ne^{-1})}$ and its abscissa is $\sqrt{(\tfrac{1}{2}n^{-1})}$. For each fixed positive x the sequence $s_1(x), s_2(x), ..., s_n(x), ...$ tends to zero as n tends to infinity. But the nearer x is to zero, the larger must we take N if, for $n \geqslant N$, all $s_n(x)$ are to be small. [$s_n(x)$ only settles down to being small *after* it has passed its peak and it will be no good considering any N which does not make $\sqrt{(\tfrac{1}{2}N^{-1})} < x$.] Hence there is not *uniform* convergence of $s_n(x)$ to its limit zero in $(0, 1)$.

$$\int_0^1 s(x)\, dx = 0, \quad \text{since } s(x) \text{ is itself zero.}$$

But

$$\int_0^1 s_n(x)\, dx = \tfrac{1}{2}[-e^{-nx^2}]_0^1 = \tfrac{1}{2}(1 - e^{-n}),$$

and this $\to \tfrac{1}{2}$ as $n \to \infty$.

EXAMPLE 2. For the sequence

$$s_n(x) = \frac{nx}{1 + n^2x^2} \quad (n = 1, 2, 3, ...),$$

$s(x) = 0$ and so $s'(x) = 0$. Also

$$s_n'(x) = \frac{n(1 - n^2x^2)}{(1 + n^2x^2)^2}.$$

When $x \neq 0$, $s_n'(x) \to 0$ as $n \to \infty$ and the formula

$$s'(x) = \lim_{n \to \infty} s_n'(x)$$

is true. But, when $x = 0$, $s_n'(x) = n$ and $\to \infty$ as $n \to \infty$.

Here it is $s_n'(x)$ that does not converge uniformly in an interval that contains $x = 0$.

4. The general convergence principle

We now state the condition for uniform convergence in a form that does not presuppose a knowledge of what $s(x)$ is. The theorem that follows is an extension of Theorem 19.

THEOREM 34. *The necessary and sufficient condition that the sequence $s_n(x)$ should converge uniformly to a limit in the interval (a, b) is that*

$$\epsilon > 0; \quad \exists \ N \ . \ \textbf{for all x in (a, b)}$$

$$|s_N(x) - s_{N+p}(x)| < \epsilon \quad \textit{for all positive integers } p.$$

To prove that the condition is necessary: In Chapter VIII, § 1.2 replace '$\exists \ N$' by '$\exists \ N$ for all x in (a, b)'; the remaining details are unaltered.

To prove that the condition is sufficient: If the condition is satisfied, then, for each fixed x in (a, b), the sequence must converge to some limit (Theorem 19). Let this limit be denoted by $s(x)$. By hypothesis,

$$\epsilon > 0; \quad \exists \ N \ . \ \textbf{for all x in (a, b)} \quad |s_N(x) - s_{N+p}(x)| < \tfrac{1}{2}\epsilon. \quad (1)$$

That is, $\qquad s_N(x) - \tfrac{1}{2}\epsilon < s_{N+p}(x) < s_N(x) + \tfrac{1}{2}\epsilon,$

and so $\quad s_N(x) - \tfrac{1}{2}\epsilon \leqslant s(x) \leqslant s_N(x) + \tfrac{1}{2}\epsilon \quad$ (Theorem 2). $\qquad (2)$

By (1) and (2), $|s(x) - s_{N+p}(x)| < \epsilon$ when p is a positive integer. Hence the condition is sufficient to ensure the uniform convergence of $s_n(x)$ to some limit $s(x)$ in (a, b).

COROLLARY 1. If $s_n(x)$ is the sum of the first n terms of an infinite series $\sum u_n(x)$, then

$$|s_N(x) - s_{N+p}(x)| \equiv |u_{N+1}(x) + ... + u_{N+p}(x)|.$$

Hence *the necessary and sufficient condition for the uniform convergence in (a, b) of the series*

$$u_1(x) + u_2(x) + ... + u_n(x) + ...$$

is that $\qquad \epsilon > 0; \quad \exists \ N \ . \ \textbf{for all x in (a, b)}$

$$|u_{N+1}(x) + ... + u_{N+p}(x)| < \epsilon \quad \textit{for all positive integers } p.$$

COROLLARY 2. *If the series of absolute values $\sum |u_n(x)|$ converges uniformly in (a, b), then so does the series $\sum u_n(x)$.*

5. Tests for uniform convergence

5.1. The M test of Weierstrass. THEOREM 35. *The series* $\sum u_n(x)$ *is uniformly convergent in* (a, b) *if we can find a convergent series of positive* CONSTANTS $\sum M_n$ *such that*

$$|u_n(x)| \leqslant M_n \quad when \ a \leqslant x \leqslant b. \tag{1}$$

Since $\sum M_n$ is convergent, we know that

$$\epsilon > 0; \quad \exists \ N \ . \ |M_{N+1} + \ldots + M_{N+p}| < \epsilon$$

for every positive integer p (Theorem 21). But

$$|u_{N+1}(x) + \ldots + u_{N+p}(x)|$$
$$\leqslant |u_{N+1}(x)| + \ldots + |u_{N+p}(x)|$$
$$\leqslant M_{N+1} + \ldots + M_{N+p} \quad when \ a \leqslant x \leqslant b,$$

by hypothesis. Hence

$$\epsilon > 0; \quad \exists \ N \ . \ \text{for all } x \text{ in } (a, b),$$

$|u_{N+1}(x) + \ldots + u_{N+p}(x)| < \epsilon$ for every positive integer p,

and so $\sum u_n(x)$ is uniformly convergent in (a, b).

5.2. Notice that, by using (1), the onus of finding an N has been removed from $\sum u_n(x)$ altogether; the onus of finding N is placed on $\sum M_n$, a series of *constants*.

5.3. Dirichlet's test. THEOREM 36. *Let*

$$s_n(x) \equiv a_1(x) + a_2(x) + \ldots + a_n(x);$$

let $v_n(x)$ *be monotonic decreasing in* n *for each fixed* x *in an interval* (a, b). *Then* $\sum a_n(x) v_n(x)$ *is uniformly convergent in* (a, b) *provided that*

(i) $\exists \ K \ . \ |s_n(x)| \leqslant K$ *for all* n *when* $a \leqslant x \leqslant b$,

(ii) $v_n(x) \to 0$ *uniformly in* (a, b).

By hypothesis (ii),

$$\epsilon, k > 0; \quad \exists \ N \ . \ \text{for all } x \text{ in } (a, b), \ |v_n(x)| < \epsilon k \quad when \ n \geqslant N.$$

Also, by Abel's lemma (cf. the proof of Theorem 24),

$$|a_{N+1}(x) v_{N+1}(x) + \ldots + a_{N+p}(x) v_{N+p}(x)| < 2K |v_{N+1}(x)| < 2Kk\epsilon.$$

The uniform convergence of $\sum a_n(x) v_n(x)$ follows from Theorem 34 if we take $k = 1/2K$.

COROLLARY. *The theorem is also true when* $v_n(x)$ *is monotonic increasing in* n *for each fixed* x *and tends uniformly to zero (through negative values) in* (a, b).

5.4. Abel's test. THEOREM 37. *Let $v_n(x)$ be either monotonic decreasing in n for each fixed x in (a, b) or monotonic increasing in n for each fixed x in (a, b). Then $\sum a_n(x)v_n(x)$ is uniformly convergent in (a, b) provided that*

(i) $\sum a_n(x)$ *is uniformly convergent in* (a, b),

(ii) $\exists\ K\ .\ |v_n(x)| < K$ *for all n when $a \leqslant x \leqslant b$.*

Since $v_n(x)$ is bounded and monotonic in n for each fixed x in (a, b), it must converge to a limit, $v(x)$ say. Write

$$u_n(x) = v(x) - v_n(x) \quad \text{or} \quad v_n(x) - v(x)$$

according as $v_n(x)$ is m.i. or m.d. Then $u_n(x)$ is positive (or zero) and is m.d. Also, by hypothesis (ii),

$$|v(x)| \leqslant K \quad \text{when } a \leqslant x \leqslant b.$$

Hence $\quad |u_n(x)| < 2K$ for all n when $a \leqslant x \leqslant b$.

By hypothesis (i),

$$\epsilon, k > 0; \quad \exists\ N\ .\ |a_{N+1}(x) + \ldots + a_{N+p}(x)| < \epsilon k$$

whenever p is a positive integer and $a \leqslant x \leqslant b$.

Hence, by Abel's lemma,

$$|a_{N+1}(x)u_{N+1}(x) + \ldots + a_{N+p}(x)u_{N+p}(x)| < \epsilon k u_{N+1}(x) < 2\epsilon kK.$$

On taking $k = 1/2K$ we see that (Theorem 34) $\sum a_n(x)u_n(x)$ is uniformly convergent in (a, b).

Also, since $|v(x)| \leqslant K$, it is easily shown (by Theorem 34) that $\sum a_n(x)v(x)$ is uniformly convergent. The uniform convergence of $\sum a_n(x)v_n(x)$ follows by the analogue for uniform convergence of Chapter VI, §3.

5.5. In many applications of these theorems either a_n or v_n does not vary with x. Suppose $\sum a_n$ is a convergent series of constants; then, for the purposes of Theorem 37, it is to be thought of as a series that is uniformly convergent in any interval whatsoever.

5.6. We shall state the analogues of Theorems 24 A and 25 A, and leave to the reader the task of amending the proofs so as to cover uniform convergence.

THEOREM 36 A.   *Let $s_n(x) \equiv a_1(x) + \ldots + a_n(x)$.   Then*
$$\sum a_n(x)v_n(x)$$
is uniformly convergent in an interval (a, b) if

(i) $\exists\ K$. $|s_n(x)| \leqslant K$ *for all n when $a \leqslant x \leqslant b$,*

(ii) $\sum |v_n(x) - v_{n+1}(x)|$ *is uniformly convergent in (a, b),*

(iii) $v_n(x) \to 0$ *uniformly in (a, b).*

THEOREM 37 A. $\sum a_n(x)v_n(x)$ *is uniformly convergent in an interval (a, b) if*

(i) $\sum a_n(x)$ *is uniformly convergent in (a, b),*

(ii) $\sum |v_n(x) - v_{n+1}(x)|$ *is convergent and its sum is bounded in (a, b),*

(iii) $\exists\ K$. $|v_n(x)| \leqslant K$ *for all n when $a \leqslant x \leqslant b$.*

EXAMPLES XVI

1. *On Theorem* 35. (i) Prove that
$$\sum \frac{x^n}{n^2}, \qquad \sum \frac{x^n}{n(n+1)}, \qquad \sum \frac{x^{2n}}{x^{2n}+n^2}$$
are uniformly convergent in $(-1, 1)$.

(ii) Prove that, if δ is any fixed number greater than unity,
$$\sum \frac{1}{x^n}, \qquad \sum \frac{1}{1+x^n}, \qquad \sum \frac{1}{x^n(1+x^n)}$$
converge uniformly with regard to all $x \geqslant \delta$, i.e. prove that
$$\epsilon > 0; \quad \exists\ N \ . \ |s(x) - s_n(x)| < \epsilon \quad \text{when } n \geqslant N \text{ and } x \geqslant \delta.$$

(iii) Prove that, if δ is any fixed positive number less than unity,
$$\sum x^n, \qquad \sum (n+1)^{-1}x^n, \qquad \sum (n+1)x^n, \qquad \sum n^3 x^n$$
converge uniformly with regard to x in $(-\delta, \delta)$.

(iv) Prove that
$$\sum \frac{1}{n^4+n^2x^2}, \qquad \sum \frac{1}{n^2+n^4x^4}$$
converge uniformly in $(-A, A)$ whatever real value A has.

HINTS. (i) $x^{2n}+n^2 > n^2$, $x^{2n}(x^{2n}+n^2)^{-1} < n^{-2}$ when $|x| \leqslant 1$.

(ii) $|x^{-n}| \leqslant \delta^{-n}$ and $\sum \delta^{-n}$ is convergent.

(iv) $n^4+n^2x^2 > n^4$.

2. *On Theorem* 36. If (v_n) is a monotonic sequence of positive constants that converges to zero, then each of the series $\sum v_n \sin n\theta$, $\sum v_n \cos n\theta$ is uniformly convergent with regard to θ in the interval $(\delta, 2\pi - \delta)$, where δ is any fixed positive number less than 2π.

3. Prove that each of the series

$$\sum \frac{\sin n\theta}{n}, \qquad \sum \frac{\cos n\theta}{n}$$

is uniformly convergent with regard to θ in $(\delta, 2\pi-\delta)$, where δ is any fixed positive number less than 2π, and that each of the series

$$\sum \frac{\sin n\theta}{n^2}, \qquad \sum \frac{\cos n\theta}{n^2}$$

is uniformly convergent with regard to θ in $(0, 2\pi)$.

4. *On Theorem* 35. Prove that the series

$$1 + \frac{e^{-2x}}{2^2-1} - \frac{e^{-4x}}{4^2-1} + \frac{e^{-6x}}{6^2-1} - \cdots$$

is uniformly convergent with regard to x in $x \geqslant 0$.

5. *On Theorem* 33. If the sum of the series in Example 4 is $f(x)$, prove that $f''(x)$ is given correctly by differentiating the series twice term by term when $x \geqslant \delta > 0$.

6. *On Theorem* 31. Prove that

$$\int_0^1 \left(\sum \frac{x^n}{n^2} \right) dx = \sum \frac{1}{n^2(n+1)}.$$

7. *On Theorem* 37. By considering $v_n(x) = x^n$, prove that $\sum a_n x^n$ is uniformly convergent in $(0, 1)$ provided that $\sum a_n$ is convergent.

8. *On Theorem* 32. Prove Theorem 29 by using the result of Example 7.

9. *On Theorem* 35. Prove that the series

$$\frac{1}{a} - \frac{2a}{a^2-1^2}\cos x + \frac{2a}{a^2-2^2}\cos 2x - \cdots$$

is uniformly convergent in any finite interval of values of x. (HINT. $|a^2-n^2| = |n^2-a^2| > \frac{1}{2}n^2$ when n exceeds a certain N.)

10. Discuss the uniform convergence of

$$\sum (-x)^n/n(1+x^n)$$

for real values of x.

11. *Extension of Theorem* 31. If the conditions of Theorem 31 are satisfied and $|F(x)| \leqslant 1$ for all x in (a, b), then

$$\int_a^b s(x)F(x)\, dx = \sum_{n=1}^{\infty} \int_a^b u_n(x)F(x)\, dx$$

provided $s(x)F(x)$ and $u_n(x)F(x)$ are integrable over (a, b).

CHAPTER XII

BINOMIAL, LOGARITHMIC, EXPONENTIAL EXPANSIONS

1. The binomial theorem

1.1. We assume the elementary theorem that

$$(1+x)^n$$
$$= 1+nx+\frac{n(n-1)}{2!}x^2+...+\frac{n(n-1)...(n-r+1)}{r!}x^r+...+x^n \quad (1)$$

when n is a positive integer. It can be proved by induction.

We use the notation

$$\binom{n}{r} \quad \text{to denote} \quad \frac{n(n-1)...(n-r+1)}{r!}$$

when r is a positive integer, whether n is an integer or not. Sometimes, for convenience, we use

$$\binom{n}{0} \quad \text{to denote} \quad 1.$$

Notice that, if n is a positive integer less than r, then $\binom{n}{r}$ is zero.

1.2. As a preliminary to our first proof of the binomial theorem when the index is not a positive integer, we now prove an identity usually known as Vandermonde's theorem.

THEOREM 38. *If r is a positive integer, then, for all values of m and n,*

$$\binom{m+n}{r} \equiv \binom{m}{r}+\binom{m}{r-1}\binom{n}{1}+...+\binom{m}{1}\binom{n}{r-1}+\binom{n}{r}. \quad (2)$$

When m and n are both positive integers, (2) follows by assuming (1) and equating coefficients of x^r in the identity

$$\sum_{r=0}^{m+n}\binom{m+n}{r}x^r = (1+x)^{m+n} = (1+x)^m.(1+x)^n$$

$$= \sum_{r=0}^{m}\binom{m}{r}x^r . \sum_{r=0}^{n}\binom{n}{r}x^r. \quad (3)$$

Now consider n, r to be fixed positive integers. Then

$$\binom{m}{r}+\binom{m}{r-1}\binom{n}{1}+\dots+\binom{m}{1}\binom{n}{r-1}+\binom{n}{r}-\binom{m+n}{r} \qquad (4)$$

is, as we see by writing out the terms in full, a polynomial of degree r in m. But, by (3), wherein m and n are any positive integers, it vanishes when $m = 1, 2, 3, \dots, r+1$. That is, the polynomial (4), of degree r in m, vanishes for $r+1$ values of m. Hence (4) is identically zero when n, r are fixed positive integers.

Now let r be a fixed positive integer and let m be fixed (integer or not). Then (4) is a polynomial, of degree r in n, that vanishes when $n = 1, 2, \dots, r+1$, that is, for $r+1$ values of n. Hence (4) is identically zero when m is fixed and r is a fixed positive integer.

Hence, when r is a fixed positive integer, (4) is zero for all values of m and n.

1.3. THEOREM 39. *If $-1 < x < 1$, the series*

$$f(x, n) = 1+nx+\frac{n(n-1)}{2!}x^2+\dots+\binom{n}{r}x^r+\dots$$

converges for all real values of n (it stops at the $(n+1)$th term if n is a positive integer) and its sum is the real positive value of $(1+x)^n$:

e.g. when $n = \frac{1}{4}$ the sum of the series is the positive fourth root of $1+x$.

By d'Alembert's ratio test, the series

$$\sum_{r=0}^{\infty}\left|\binom{n}{r}x^r\right|$$

is convergent for all real n when $|x| < 1$. By the multiplication of absolutely convergent series (Theorem 27),

$$f(x, n) . f(x, m) = \sum_{r=0}^{\infty} c_r x^r,$$

where $\quad c_r = \binom{m}{r}+\binom{m}{r-1}\binom{n}{1}+\dots+\binom{m}{1}\binom{n}{r-1}+\binom{n}{r},$

whenever m, n are real and $|x| < 1$.

But, by Vandermonde's theorem, $c_r = \binom{m+n}{r}$. Hence, when $|x| < 1$,

$$f(x, n) . f(x, m) = \sum_{r=0}^{\infty} \binom{m+n}{r} x^r = f(x, m+n). \quad (5)$$

By induction

$$f(x, n) . f(x, m) ... f(x, \lambda) = f(x, m+n+...+\lambda),$$

$$\{f(x, n)\}^k = f(x, nk) \quad (k \text{ a positive integer}). \quad (6)$$

Further, $f(x, n) . f(x, -n) = f(x, 0) = 1,$ (7)

since the series for $f(x, n)$ reduces to 1 when $n = 0$.

If n is a positive fraction p/q, then (6) gives

$$\{f(x, p/q)\}^q = f(x, p) = (1+x)^p$$

since p is a positive integer. Hence, when $|x| < 1$ [(5), (6), (7) have been proved only when this condition is satisfied],

$$f(x, p/q) \quad \text{is a value of} \quad (1+x)^{p/q}.$$

Moreover, if $0 < \delta < 1$, the series for $f(x, n)$ is (by the M test) uniformly convergent in $0 \leqslant |x| \leqslant \delta$: each term is continuous in x, and so, by Theorem 32, $f(x, n)$ is continuous in $(-\delta, \delta)$. But $f(0, n) = 1$, and so $f(x, p/q)$ is that value of $(1+x)^{p/q}$ which tends to 1 as x tends to zero; and this value is the positive qth root of $(1+x)^p$.

In virtue of (7) the same result holds when p is replaced by $-p$. Hence, if n is a positive or negative rational number, and $-1 < x < 1$, then

$$1 + nx + \frac{n(n-1)}{2!} x^2 + ... + \binom{n}{r} x^r + ... = (1+x)^n \quad (|x| < 1),$$

the positive root being taken.

The proof of the theorem for n not rational, by means of a limiting process, is not an easy proof. A proof by a different method will be given after we have dealt with the exponential function.

2. The exponential function

2.1. We define e to be the sum of the series

$$1 + 1 + \frac{1}{2!} + \frac{1}{3!} + ... + \frac{1}{n!} + ..., \quad (8)$$

and consider the series

$$1+x+\frac{x^2}{2!}+\frac{x^3}{3!}+\dots+\frac{x^n}{n!}+\dots. \qquad (9)$$

The series (9) is

(i) absolutely convergent for all values of x,

(ii) uniformly convergent in any finite interval $(-A, A)$.

(The series $\sum A^n/n!$ converges, by Theorem 10, and (ii) follows by the M test (Theorem 35).)

Let $E(x)$ denote the sum of the series (9), so that $E(1) = e$, $E(0) = 1$.

2.2. The relation between $E(x)$ and e^x. Rational numbers. By the multiplication of absolutely convergent series (Theorem 27),

$$E(x).E(y) = \sum_{r=0}^{\infty}\left\{\frac{x^r}{r!}+\frac{x^{r-1}y}{(r-1)!\,1!}+\frac{x^{r-2}y^2}{(r-2)!\,2!}+\dots+\frac{y^r}{r!}\right\}$$

$$= \sum_{r=0}^{\infty}\frac{(x+y)^r}{r!} = E(x+y),$$

for all real values of x and y. As in the proof of the binomial expansion, this gives

$$E(n) = \{E(1)\}^n = e^n, \qquad (10\,a)$$

$$E\!\left(\frac{p}{q}\right) = \text{a value of } \sqrt[q]{(e^p)} \quad \text{i.e. of } e^{p/q}, \qquad (10\,b)$$

$$E\!\left(\frac{p}{q}\right).E\!\left(-\frac{p}{q}\right) = E(0) = 1. \qquad (10\,c)$$

That is to say, when x is a rational number, $E(x)$ is a value of e^x, and, by continuity, it is that value of e^x which $\to 1$ as $x \to 0$.

Irrational numbers. Since the series (9) is unaltered when it is differentiated with regard to x, the differentiated series converges uniformly in any finite interval $(-A, A)$. Hence, by Theorem 33,

$$\frac{d}{dx}E(x) = E(x);$$

also, for any given x, $E(x)$ is a finite number. That is to say,

$$\frac{E(x+h)-E(x)}{h} \to \text{a finite limit as } h \to 0.$$

Accordingly, $E(x+h)$ must tend to $E(x)$ as $h \to 0$; for if it did not, then $\{E(x+h)-E(x)\}/h$ could not tend to a finite limit. (In words, a function with a finite differential coefficient must be continuous.)

If x is irrational and (α_n) is a m.i. sequence of rational numbers that tends to x, then, by what we have proved,

$$E(x) = \lim_{\alpha_n \to x} E(\alpha_n) = \lim_{\alpha_n \to x} e^{\alpha_n}. \tag{11}$$

It is now a matter of indifference whether

(i) we define e^x as $E(x)$ and deduce $e^x = \lim_{\alpha_n \to x} e^{\alpha_n}$,

or (ii) we define e^x as $\lim_{\alpha_n \to x} e^{\alpha_n}$ and deduce $e^x = E(x)$.

With either definition we have $e^x \times e^y = e^{x+y}$, $e^x > e^y$ when $x > y$, $e^{x_n} \to e^x$ when $x_n \to x$, and so on.

3. Logarithms

It follows from (10) and (11) of § 2 that

$$e^y \text{ is positive if } y \text{ is real.} \tag{12}$$

If $e^y = x$, we write $y = \log x$, thus defining the logarithm of any positive number. By the differential calculus

$$1 = e^y \frac{dy}{dx}, \quad \text{or} \quad \frac{d}{dx}(\log x) = \frac{1}{x}.$$

Also, $\log 1 = 0$ since $E(0) = 1$, so that, when $x > 0$,

$$\int_1^x \frac{dt}{t} = \log x,$$

an equation which is frequently taken as the definition of a logarithm.

From § 2 it follows that, when x_1, x_2 are positive,

$$\log(x_1 x_2) = \log x_1 + \log x_2,$$

and so on. There is one detail which should be noted particularly, and that is

'if $\log x_n \to y$, then $x_n \to e^y$'.

To see the truth of this statement, let $\log x_n = y_n$, so that $y_n \to y$ and $x_n = e^{y_n}$. But, as we saw in § 2.2, $E(y+h) \to E(y)$ as $h \to 0$, and so $E(y_n) \to E(y)$ as $y_n \to y$; that is, $e^{y_n} \to e^y$.

4. The function a^x when a is positive

Rational index. If x is a rational number, p/q say, then

$$a^{p/q} = (e^{\log a})^{p/q} \quad \text{(by the definition of logarithm)}$$
$$= \{E(\log a)\}^{p/q}$$
$$= E\{(p/q)\log a\} = e^{(p/q)\log a},$$

by the results established in §2.

Irrational index. If x is an irrational number we take $e^{x \log a}$ as our definition of a^x. Thus, whether x is rational or irrational,

$$a^x = e^{x \log a}. \tag{13}$$

If x is an irrational number and (α_n) is a m.i. sequence of rational numbers that tends to x, then, by (11),

$$\lim_{\alpha_n \to x} (a^{\alpha_n}) = \lim_{\alpha_n \to x} (e^{\alpha_n \log a}) = e^{x \log a} = a^x.$$

We also have $a^x \times a^y = a^{x+y}$, and so on, whether x, y are rational or irrational.

A point in the differential calculus. When x is positive and n is any real constant we have, using the equation (13),

$$\frac{d}{dx}(x^n) = \frac{d}{dx}(e^{n\log x})$$
$$= e^{n\log x}.n\frac{d}{dx}(\log x)$$
$$= x^n.\frac{n}{x} = nx^{n-1}.$$

Thus if $z > -1$, and if μ is any real constant, then

$$\frac{d}{dz}(1+z)^\mu = \mu(1+z)^{\mu-1}\frac{d(1+z)}{dz} = \mu(1+z)^{\mu-1}, \tag{14}$$

a result of fundamental importance to the work that follows.

5. The binomial theorem for any real index

The proof we are about to give is one that depends, essentially, on a prior establishment of (14). The point is of some logical interest: we can, if we so wish, find a proof of the binomial theorem for any index and then use the binomial theorem in proving (14) for any index; alternatively, we can make our proof of (14) independent of the binomial theorem and then use (14) to prove the binomial theorem. Some care is necessary to ensure that we do not use each to prove the other.

Consider the series

$$1 + \mu x + \frac{\mu(\mu-1)}{2!} x^2 + \ldots + \binom{\mu}{r} x^r + \ldots, \qquad (15)$$

where μ is any fixed real number.

If k is any fixed positive number less than unity, and if $-k \leqslant x \leqslant k$, then

$$\left| \binom{\mu}{r} x^r \right| \leqslant \left| \binom{\mu}{r} \right| k^r,$$

and $\qquad \left| \binom{\mu}{r} \right| k^r \div \left| \binom{\mu}{r+1} \right| k^{r+1} = \left| \frac{r+1}{\mu-r} \right| \frac{1}{k} \to \frac{1}{k} \quad$ as $r \to \infty.$

Hence, by Theorem 10 and the M test, the series (15) converges uniformly in $(-k, k)$ for any fixed μ.

The series obtained by differentiating (15) term by term is

$$\mu \left[1 + (\mu-1)x + \ldots + \binom{\mu-1}{r} x^r + \ldots \right]$$

and so converges uniformly in $(-k, k)$. Hence, by Theorem 33, if $f(x)$ denotes the sum of (15), and if $-k < x < k$, then

$$f'(x) = \mu \sum_{r=0}^{\infty} \binom{\mu-1}{r} x^r,$$

and $\qquad xf'(x) = \mu \sum_{r=1}^{\infty} \binom{\mu-1}{r-1} x^r.$

But, if $r \geqslant 1$, then

$$\binom{\mu-1}{r} + \binom{\mu-1}{r-1} = \binom{\mu}{r}.$$

Hence $\qquad f'(x) + xf'(x) = \mu \left\{ 1 + \sum_{r=1}^{\infty} \binom{\mu}{r} x^r \right\},$

that is, $\qquad (1+x)f'(x) - \mu f(x) = 0.$

Hence, *assuming that* (14) *is true* (as we have proved it is),

$$\frac{d}{dx} \left\{ \frac{f(x)}{(1+x)^\mu} \right\} = 0.$$

Hence $\qquad f(x) = A(1+x)^\mu,$

where A is a constant, independent of x. But $f(0) = 1$. Hence, if by $(1+x)^{\mu}$ we mean the real positive value of $(1+x)^{\mu}$, which reduces to 1 when $x = 0$, then $A = 1$; and so

$$(1+x)^{\mu} = 1 + \mu x + \frac{\mu(\mu-1)}{2!}x^2 + \ldots + \binom{\mu}{r}x^r + \ldots \qquad (16)$$

for all real values of μ.

Finally, (16) has been proved when $-k < x < k$ and k is any fixed number less than unity. Hence (16) is true for every x such that $-1 < x < 1$. For, if we take any definite x in $)-1, 1($, we can choose a k less than unity so that this x lies in $)-k, k($. (The statement becomes obvious on drawing a line and marking the points $-1, x, 1$ on it.)

6. General remarks on §§ 1–5

We have tried to give a logical framework for the development and interdependence of the binomial, exponential, and logarithmic functions. We have made no attempt to develop *all* the properties of exponential and logarithmic functions from the definitions. The reader will probably be familiar with these properties. He can, if he so wishes, develop them, and that without any serious difficulty, from the definitions here adopted.

7. The binomial series when $x = 1$ and when $x = -1$

We have seen that, when $-1 < x < 1$ and μ is real,

$$1 + \mu x + \frac{\mu(\mu-1)}{2!}x^2 + \ldots + \binom{\mu}{n}x^n + \ldots \qquad (1)$$

is (absolutely) convergent and that its sum is the positive value of $(1+x)^{\mu}$. When $x = 1$, the series becomes

$$1 + \mu + \frac{\mu(\mu-1)}{2!} + \ldots + \frac{\mu(\mu-1)\ldots(\mu-n+1)}{n!} + \ldots. \qquad (2)$$

When n exceeds $\mu+1$, the factors $\mu-n+1$, $\mu-n+2,\ldots$ are all negative, so that the terms of (2) are ultimately of alternate signs. Write

$$v_n = (-1)^n \frac{\mu(\mu-1)\ldots(\mu-n+1)}{n!}.$$

Then we have

$$\frac{v_n}{v_{n+1}} = -\frac{n+1}{\mu-n} = \frac{n+1}{n-\mu} = 1 + \frac{\mu+1}{n-\mu}.$$

Hence, if $\mu+1 > 0$, the sequence (v_n) is m.d. when $n > \mu$. Also, when $n > \mu > -1$,

$$n-\mu < n+1 \quad \text{and} \quad \frac{1}{n-\mu} > \frac{1}{n+1},$$

so that $\dfrac{v_n}{v_{n+p}} > \left(1+\dfrac{\mu+1}{n+1}\right)\left(1+\dfrac{\mu+1}{n+2}\right)\cdots\left(1+\dfrac{\mu+1}{n+p}\right)$

$$> 1+(\mu+1)\left(\frac{1}{n+1}+\frac{1}{n+2}+\dots+\frac{1}{n+p}\right). \tag{3}$$

Now let $p \to \infty$, *keeping n fixed*. Since $\sum(1/n)$ is divergent, the expression (3) $\to \infty$ as $p \to \infty$, and so $v_{n+p} \to 0$ as $p \to \infty$.

Hence the sequence (v_n) is ultimately m.d. and $v_n \to 0$ as $n \to \infty$. Hence, by Theorem 18, $\sum(-1)^n v_n$ is convergent; that is, the series (2) is convergent if $\mu+1 > 0$. Further, when $0 < x < 1$, the sum of the series (1) is $(1+x)^\mu$ and $\to 2^\mu$ as $x \to 1$ from values less than 1. Hence, by Theorem 29, the sum of the series (2) is 2^μ when $\mu+1 > 0$.

We have thus proved that, when $\mu > -1$,

$$1+\mu+\frac{\mu(\mu-1)}{2!}+\dots+\binom{\mu}{n}+\dots = 2^\mu. \tag{4}$$

When $x = -1$ the series (1) becomes

$$1-\mu+\frac{\mu(\mu-1)}{2!}-\dots. \tag{5}$$

This series we have considered in Examples VII, 1. It is convergent when $\mu > 0$. By Theorem 29, its sum is given by

$$\lim_{x \to 1}(1-x)^\mu, \quad \text{i.e. } 0.$$

Hence, when $\mu > 0$,

$$1-\mu+\frac{\mu(\mu-1)}{2!}-\dots = 0. \tag{6}$$

8. The logarithmic expansion

As we have seen in §3,

$$\int_1^x \frac{d\theta}{\theta} = \log x \quad (x > 0).$$

Put $x = 1+y$, $\theta = 1+t$, and we get

$$\int_0^y \frac{dt}{1+t} = \log(1+y) \quad (y > -1).$$

By elementary algebra,

$$\frac{1-z^n}{1-z} = 1+z+\ldots+z^{n-1},$$

or

$$\frac{1}{1-z} = 1+z+\ldots+z^{n-1}+\frac{z^n}{1-z}.$$

On writing $z = -t$, this becomes

$$\frac{1}{1+t} = 1-t+t^2-\ldots+(-t)^{n-1}+(-1)^n\frac{t^n}{1+t}.$$

Hence

$$\log(1+y) = y-\frac{y^2}{2}+\frac{y^3}{3}+\ldots+(-1)^{n-1}\frac{y^n}{n}+(-1)^n\int_0^y\frac{t^n\,dt}{1+t}.$$

But, when $y > 0$, so that $1+t > 1$ throughout the range of integration,

$$\left|\int_0^y \frac{t^n\,dt}{1+t}\right| < \int_0^y t^n\,dt = \frac{y^{n+1}}{n+1},$$

and this $\to 0$ as $n \to \infty$ if $0 < y \leqslant 1$.

Also, if $0 > y > -1$, so that

$$1+t > 1+y > 0$$

throughout the range of integration, we have

$$\left|\int_0^y \frac{(-)^n t^n\,dt}{1+t}\right| < \frac{1}{1+y}\int_0^{|y|} t^n\,dt = \frac{|y|^{n+1}}{(n+1)(1+y)},$$

which $\to 0$ as $n \to \infty$. (Notice that the argument breaks down if $y = -1$.)

Hence, if $-1 < y \leqslant 1$, the series

$$y-\tfrac{1}{2}y^2+\tfrac{1}{3}y^3-\tfrac{1}{4}y^4+\ldots$$

converges to $\log(1+y)$.

9. Some useful inequalities

Consider the graph $y = t^{-1}$, P the point $(1, 1)$ on it, and Q

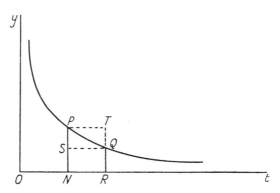

the point (x, x^{-1}) on it, where $x > 1$. Since t^{-1} becomes steadily less as t increases, it is clear that

$$\text{rect. } NQ < \text{area } PNRQ < \text{rect. } NT.$$

That is, when $x > 1$,

$$\frac{x-1}{x} < \int_{1}^{x} \frac{dt}{t} < x-1,$$

i.e.

$$\frac{x-1}{x} < \log x < x-1 \quad (x > 1), \tag{1}$$

or

$$\frac{x}{x+1} < \log(1+x) < x \quad (x > 0). \tag{2}$$

In (1) put $x = (1-\xi)^{-1}$, where $0 < \xi < 1$; we get

$$\xi < \log \frac{1}{1-\xi} < \frac{\xi}{1-\xi} \quad (0 < \xi < 1). \tag{3}$$

The inequalities (2) and (3) enable us to show that

$$\lim_{n \to \infty} \left(1 + \frac{x}{n}\right)^n = e^x \tag{4}$$

for all real values of x. For, if $x > 0$, then (2) gives

$$\frac{x}{x+n} < \log\left(1 + \frac{x}{n}\right) < \frac{x}{n},$$

i.e.

$$\frac{nx}{n+x} < n \log\left(1 + \frac{x}{n}\right) < x. \tag{5}$$

Since
$$\frac{nx}{n+x} \to x \quad \text{as } n \to \infty,$$

it follows that $n\log(1+x/n) \to x$ as $n \to \infty$, and so, by § 3, (4) follows when $x > 0$.

When x is negative, equal to $-\xi$ say, and we take n large enough to make $(\xi/n) < 1$, (3) gives

$$\frac{\xi}{n} < -\log\left(1-\frac{\xi}{n}\right) < \frac{\xi}{n-\xi},$$

i.e. on multiplying throughout by $-n$,

$$x > n\log\left(1+\frac{x}{n}\right) > \frac{nx}{n+x}, \tag{6}$$

which is (5) with the inequality signs reversed.

We conclude with an 'inequality theorem' that has frequent and diverse applications.

THEOREM 40. *If k is any fixed positive number, then*

$$\frac{e^x}{x^k} \to \infty \quad as \ x \to \infty,$$

$$\frac{\log x}{x^k} \to 0 \quad as \ x \to \infty.$$

In the first place, if x is positive and M is an integer that exceeds k, say $M-k = \alpha > 0$,

$$e^x > 1+x+\frac{x^2}{2!}+...+\frac{x^M}{M!}.$$

Hence
$$\frac{e^x}{x^k} > \frac{x^{M-k}}{M!} = \frac{x^\alpha}{M!} \quad (\alpha > 0).$$

As x increases indefinitely, so does x^α, and, M being fixed, the first part of the theorem follows.

Next, if $x > 1$, then (1) gives

$$0 < \log x < x-1 < x,$$

so that, if n is positive, and $x > 1$,

$$n\log x = \log x^n < x^n.$$

Hence
$$\frac{\log x}{x^k} < \frac{x^n}{nx^k},$$

or, on taking $n = \frac{1}{2}k$,

$$\frac{\log x}{x^k} < \frac{2}{kx^{\frac{1}{2}k}}.$$

But, k being fixed and positive, the last expression tends to zero as x tends to infinity, and the second part of the theorem follows.

Notice that $\log x \to \infty$ as $x \to \infty$; for if $x > e^n$,

$$\log x > \log e^n = n.$$

Theorem 40 is often useful in the forms

(i) e^x tends to infinity faster than any power of x,

(ii) $\log x$ tends to infinity more slowly than any power of x.

NOTE. The formal definitions for convergence, divergence when $x \to \infty$ through values which are not necessarily the integers $1, 2, 3, ..., n, ...$ are, in the notation introduced in Chapter II,

(i) $f(x) \to l$ as $x \to \infty$ if

$$\epsilon > 0; \quad \exists\ X\ .\ |f(x) - l| < \epsilon \quad \text{when } x > X,$$

(ii) $f(x) \to \infty$ as $x \to \infty$ if

$$A > 0; \quad \exists\ X\ .\ f(x) > A \quad \text{when } x > X.$$

EXAMPLES XVII

1. Expand $(2+x)^{-1}$ as a power series in x.

The binomial theorem when the index is not a positive integer refers only to the expansion of $(1+x)^n$. To expand $(2+x)^{-1}$ we proceed as follows:

$$(2+x)^{-1} = 2^{-1}(1+\tfrac{1}{2}x)^{-1}$$
$$= \tfrac{1}{2}\{1 - \tfrac{1}{2}x + (\tfrac{1}{2}x)^2 - (\tfrac{1}{2}x)^3 + ...\},$$

when $|\tfrac{1}{2}x| < 1$, that is, when $|x| < 2$.

2. Prove that, when $|x| < 1$,

$$(1-x)^{-\frac{1}{2}} = 1 + \frac{1}{2}x + \frac{1.3}{2.4}x^2 + ... + \frac{1.3...(2n-1)}{2.4...2n}x^n + ...,$$

$$(1-x)^{\frac{1}{2}} = 1 - \frac{1}{2}x - \frac{1}{2.4}x^2 - ... - \frac{1.3...(2n-3)}{2.4...2n}x^n - ....$$

NOTE. It is worth while to be able to recognize the R.H.S. as the series which represents the L.H.S.

3. Prove that, when $|x| < 1$,

$$(1-x)^{-m} = 1 + \sum_{n=1}^{\infty} \frac{m(m+1)...(m+n-1)}{n!}x^n.$$

4. Prove that, when $|x| < 1$,

$$(1+x)^{\frac{1}{2}m} = 1 + \frac{m}{2}x + \frac{m(m-2)}{2.4}x^2 + \dots .$$

5. Prove that, when $|x| < 1$,

$$(1-x)^{-2} = 1 + 2x + 3x^2 + 4x^3 + \dots ,$$

$$(1-x)^{-3} = 1 + 3x + 6x^2 + \dots + \tfrac{1}{2}(n+1)(n+2)x^n + \dots .$$

6. Various identities can be obtained in a manner similar to the following:

$$\frac{(1-x)^m}{1-x} = (1-x)^{m-1}.$$

Hence

$$\left\{1 - \binom{m}{1}x + \binom{m}{2}x^2 - \dots + (-)^n\binom{m}{n}x^n + \dots\right\}\{1 + x + x^2 + \dots\}$$

$$= 1 - \binom{m-1}{1}x + \binom{m-1}{2}x^2 - \dots + (-)^n\binom{m-1}{n}x^n + \dots$$

when $|x| < 1$. Multiply the first two series: Theorem 27 gives, on equating coefficients,

$$1 - \binom{m}{1} + \binom{m}{2} - \dots + (-)^n\binom{m}{n} = (-)^n\binom{m-1}{n}.$$

NOTE. See Theorem 47, which justifies the step of equating coefficients in two power series.

7. Establish identities by considering

$$\frac{(1-x)^m}{(1-x)^2} = (1-x)^{m-2}, \qquad (1+x)^m(1+x)^2 = (1+x)^{m+2}.$$

8. When n is a positive integer, prove that

$$\sum_{r=1}^{n}(-1)^r r\binom{n}{r} = 0,$$

and prove also that

$$\sum_{r=1}^{n}(-1)^r r^m\binom{n}{r} = 0 \quad \text{when } m = 1, 2, \dots, n-1.$$

9. If $f(x) = \prod(x - a_r)$, a product of n different factors, and $\phi(x)$ is of degree less than n, prove that

$$\frac{\phi(x)}{f(x)} = \sum_{r=1}^{n}\frac{\phi'(a_r)}{f'(a_r)}\frac{1}{x - a_r},$$

and hence show that when $|x|$ is sufficiently small

$$\frac{\phi(x)}{f(x)} = -\sum_{k=0}^{\infty}x^k\left\{\sum_{r=1}^{n}\frac{\phi(a_r)}{f'(a_r)}a_r^{-k-1}\right\},$$

and that when $|x|$ is sufficiently large

$$\frac{\phi(x)}{f(x)} = \sum_{k=0}^{\infty} x^{-k-1} \left\{ \sum_{r=1}^{n} \frac{\phi(a_r)}{f'(a_r)} a_r^k \right\}.$$

10. Show, by using partial fractions, that

$$\frac{5x^2 - 16x + 13}{(x-1)(x-2)(3x-5)}$$

can be expanded in a series of ascending powers of x when $|x| < 1$, and find the coefficient of x^n in this expansion.

11. Prove (i) that the series whose nth term is

$$\frac{1}{n} - \frac{1}{2n+1} - \frac{1}{2n+2}$$

is convergent, (ii) that its sum is $\frac{3}{2} - \log 2$.

12. Expand $\log(1 + x^3)$ and $\log(1 - x + x^2)$ in powers of x.

13. If n is a positive integer, expand $\log(1 + n^{-1})$ as a power series in $\{1/(2n+1)\}$.

14. Show that, if powers of x above the sixth can be neglected,

$$(120 + 60x + 12x^2 + x^3) \div (120 - 60x + 12x^2 - x^3)$$

is equal to e^x.

15. Multiply the expansions of $(1-x)^{-1}$ and $\log(1-x)$, and deduce by integration that

$$\tfrac{1}{2}[\log(1-x)]^2 = \tfrac{1}{2}x^2 + \tfrac{1}{3}(1 + \tfrac{1}{2})x^3 + \tfrac{1}{4}(1 + \tfrac{1}{2} + \tfrac{1}{3})x^4 + \dots.$$

16. Determine the expansion of $\log(1+x).\log(1-x)$ either by direct multiplication, or by expanding the differential coefficient.

17. Prove that, when $x > 1$,

$$(1+x)^{-\frac{1}{2}} = x^{-\frac{1}{2}} - \frac{1}{2}x^{-\frac{3}{2}} + \frac{1.3}{2.4}x^{-\frac{5}{2}} - \dots.$$

CHAPTER XIII

POWER SERIES

1. Series of complex terms

1.1. We assume that the reader is familiar with the complex number $z = x+iy$, or, on writing $x = r\cos\theta$ and $y = r\sin\theta$, $z = r(\cos\theta + i\sin\theta)$; and that he is familiar with the representation of complex numbers in an Argand diagram.

DEFINITION. *A sequence of complex numbers*
$$z_n = x_n + iy_n \quad (n = 1, 2, ...),$$
is said to converge to $z = x+iy$, *if* $x_n \to x$ *and* $y_n \to y$.

DEFINITION. *A series of complex numbers*
$$\sum u_n, \quad \text{where } u_n = v_n + iw_n,$$
is said to converge if the sequence (s_n) *converges, where*
$$s_n \equiv u_1 + u_2 + ... + u_n.$$

Thus a necessary and sufficient condition for the convergence of $\sum u_n$ is the convergence of each of the series $\sum v_n$, $\sum w_n$.

DEFINITION. *If* $z = x+iy = r(\cos\theta + i\sin\theta)$, *then*
$$|z| \equiv r = +\sqrt{(x^2+y^2)} \text{ is called the MODULUS of } z,$$
and $\arg z \equiv \theta$ *is called the* ARGUMENT *of* z.

1.2. We shall not go very fully into the theory of series of complex terms,† but we develop certain results which are necessary in the theory of power series.

THEOREM 41. *If* $u_n = v_n + iw_n$, *so that*
$$|u_n| = \sqrt{(v_n^2 + w_n^2)},$$
and if $\sum |u_n|$ *is convergent, then* $\sum u_n$ *is convergent. If* $\sum |u_n|$ *is convergent, then* $\sum u_n$ *is said to be absolutely convergent.*

For $|v_n| = +\sqrt{(v_n^2)} < |u_n|$, and so, by Theorem 8 (the comparison test), $\sum |v_n|$ converges when $\sum |u_n|$ converges. Similarly, $\sum |w_n|$ converges when $\sum |u_n|$ converges.

Hence, when $\sum |u_n|$ is convergent, both $\sum v_n$ and $\sum w_n$ are convergent.

---

† The topic is more fully treated in E. T. Copson's book on *Functions of a Complex Variable* (Oxford University Press, 1935).

THEOREM 42. *If $\sum u_n$ is convergent, then $|u_n| \to 0$ as $n \to \infty$.*
Because $|u_n| \to 0$ it does NOT *follow that $\sum u_n$ is convergent.*

If $u_n = v_n + iw_n$, and if $\sum u_n$ is convergent, then both $\sum v_n$ and $\sum w_n$ are convergent. By Theorem 14, $v_n \to 0$ and $w_n \to 0$, so that $|u_n| \to 0$.

The series
$$\sum \left(\frac{1}{n} + \frac{i}{n^2}\right)$$

is not convergent; its nth term $\to 0$ as $n \to \infty$.

2. Power series

2.1. We shall use a_n to denote a number that depends on n but not on z, and the power series we shall consider is

$$\sum_{n=0}^{\infty} a_n z^n = a_0 + a_1 z + \ldots + a_n z^n + \ldots. \tag{1}$$

This series we shall usually denote by $\sum a_n z^n$.

The most important fact about such a series is that either

   (i) it converges for no value of z other than $z = 0$,

or (ii) it converges for all values of z,

or (iii) there is a finite number R, dependent on the coefficients a_n, such that

$$\sum |a_n z^n| \quad \text{and so, also,} \quad \sum a_n z^n$$

is convergent when $|z| < R$, and

$$\sum |a_n z^n| \quad \text{is divergent when } |z| > R.$$

We first establish the theorem on which this fact depends.

THEOREM 43. *If, for a given z_0, $\sum a_n z_0^n$ is convergent, then $\sum a_n z^n$ is absolutely convergent when $|z| < |z_0|$.*

Since $\sum a_n z_0^n$ is convergent, we have (by Theorem 42)

$$|a_n z_0^n| \to 0 \quad as \ n \to \infty.$$

Hence $\exists \ N$. $|a_n z_0^n| < \frac{1}{2}$ when $n \geqslant N$,

and $|a_n z^n| < \frac{1}{2}|z/z_0|^n$ when $n \geqslant N$.

But $\sum |z/z_0|^n$ is convergent when $|z/z_0| < 1$, and so (by Theorems 8 and 13) $\sum |a_n z^n|$ is convergent when $|z| < |z_0|$.

2.2. Now suppose $\sum a_n z^n$ converges for at least one value of z other than $z = 0$, so that the alternative (i) of § 2.1 is ruled out. Let the series converge when $z = z_0$, and let $|z_0| = r_0$. Then, by Theorem 43, it converges when $|z| = r$ if $r < r_0$.

Now suppose, further, that $\sum a_n z^n$ does not converge for all values of z, so that the alternative (ii) of § 2.1 is ruled out. Let the series be non-convergent when $z = z_1$, and let $|z_1| = r_1$. Then the numbers r such that $\sum |a_n z^n|$ is convergent when $|z| = r$ must have a finite upper bound $\leqslant r_1$. Let this upper bound be R.

This number R is, by definition of upper bound, the least number that is greater than or equal to each and every r for which $\sum |a_n z^n|$ is convergent when $|z| = r$.

It may be that R is actually greater than every such r; it may be that R is itself a possible value of r. Thus, ALWAYS, $\sum a_n z^n$ is absolutely convergent when $|z| < R$, and, POSSIBLY, $\sum a_n z^n$ is absolutely convergent when $|z| = R$.

Finally, $\sum a_n z^n$ cannot converge for any z whose modulus exceeds R. For, suppose it converges for a z whose modulus is $R+\alpha$, where $\alpha > 0$; then, by Theorem 43, $\sum |a_n z^n|$ is convergent whenever $|z| = R+\frac{1}{2}\alpha$, so that $R+\frac{1}{2}\alpha$ is a possible value of the r, and R is not the upper bound of the r.

We have thus proved that, corresponding to every power series, $\sum a_n z^n$, which converges for some non-zero value of z but not for all values of z, there is a number R such that

$$\sum |a_n z^n| \quad \text{is convergent when } |z| < R,$$
$$\sum |a_n z^n| \quad \text{is divergent when } |z| > R.$$

This number R is called the **radius of convergence** of the power series.

Whether or not $\sum |a_n z^n|$ converges when $|z| = R$ depends entirely upon the character of the sequence (a_n). For example, both the series

$$\sum \left| \frac{z^n}{n^2} \right|, \qquad \sum \left| \frac{z^n}{n} \right|.$$

converge when $|z| < 1$ and diverge when $|z| > 1$ (as is seen by Theorem 10, the ratio test). When $|z| = 1$, the first series converges, while the second diverges.

2.3. The radius of convergence is given by

$$\underline{\lim} \ |a_n|^{-1/n},$$

but we shall not go into the proof of this, as $\underline{\lim}$ is outside the scope of our present treatment of convergence.

In examples we confine our attention to power series (and these are by far the most common type) whose radii of convergence can be determined by other means, usually by the ratio tests.

2.4. THEOREM 44. *The series obtained by differentiating or integrating a power series term by term have the same radius of convergence as the original series.*

If the original series converges for all z, so do the differentiated and integrated series.

Let R be the radius of convergence of $\sum a_n z^n$. Let z be any complex number (not zero) whose modulus, r, is less than R. Choose z_1 so that $r < |z_1| < R$ [say, for example,

$$|z_1| = \tfrac{1}{2}(r+R).]$$

Then $\sum |a_n z_1^n|$ is convergent, so that $|a_n z_1^n| \to 0$, and

$$\exists \ N \ . \ |a_n z_1^n| < \tfrac{1}{2} \quad \text{when } n \geqslant N.$$

When $n \geqslant N$,

$$|na_n z^{n-1}| = \frac{1}{|z|} \left| n\left(\frac{z}{z_1}\right)^n \right| . \, |a_n z_1^n|$$

$$< \frac{1}{2r} n |z/z_1|^n.$$

But the series $\sum n\rho^n$ is convergent when $|\rho| < 1$, so that, since $|z| < |z_1|$, $\sum n|z/z_1|^n$ is convergent. Hence (by Theorems 8 and 13) $\sum |na_n z^{n-1}|$ is convergent, and so $\sum na_n z^{n-1}$ is absolutely convergent whenever $|z| < R$.

Similarly, $\sum a_n z^{n+1}/(n+1)$ is absolutely convergent whenever $|z| < R$.

Now suppose that the radius of convergence of $\sum na_n z^{n-1}$ is greater than R and equal to R_1, say. Then, on integrating *this* series, the series $\sum a_n z^n$ is absolutely convergent when $|z| < R_1$. But this is incompatible with the assumption that $\sum |a_n z^n|$

diverges when $|z| > R$. Hence the radius of convergence of $\sum na_n z^{n-1}$ cannot exceed R.

Similarly, the radius of convergence of the integrated series cannot exceed R.

This proves the theorem when the original series has a finite radius of convergence. If the original series converges for all values of z we may, by the previous work, show that $\sum na_n z^{n-1}$ and $\sum a_n z^{n+1}/(n+1)$ converge absolutely when $|z| < A$, where A is any number we choose. Hence these series also converge for all values of z.

2.5. For our remaining theorems we shall confine ourselves to real values of z.

THEOREM 45. *If the radius of convergence of $\sum a_n x^n$ is R, then $\sum a_n x^n$ is uniformly convergent in $(-R_1, R_1)$, where R_1 is any fixed positive number* LESS THAN *R.*

In special cases it may be uniformly convergent in $(-R, R)$: in general, it is not.

Let R_1 be any fixed positive number less than R. Then $\sum |a_n R_1^n|$ is convergent. But

$$|a_n x^n| \leqslant |a_n R_1^n| \quad \text{when } |x| \leqslant R_1,$$

and the M test proves the theorem.

In the special case when $\sum |a_n R^n|$ is convergent, the M test proves uniform convergence in $(-R, R)$. We have only to consider the series $\sum x^n$ to see that $(-R, R)$ is not, in general, an interval of uniform convergence; for then $R = 1$ and the series diverges when $x = 1$.

COROLLARY. *If $\sum a_n x^n$ has a radius of convergence R, and if $f(x)$ denotes the sum of the series when $|x| < R$, then*

$$f'(x) = \sum n a_n x^{n-1},$$

$$\int_0^x f(t)\, dt = \sum a_n \frac{x^{n+1}}{n+1}$$

whenever $|x| < R$.

Let x have any definite value whose modulus, r, is less than R. In Theorem 45 take $R_1 = \frac{1}{2}(r+R)$, so that $|x| < R_1$;

$\sum a_n x^n$ and (by Theorem 44) $\sum n a_n x^{n-1}$ are uniformly convergent in $(-R_1, R_1)$. The two parts of the corollary follow by Theorems 33, 31 respectively.

2.6. The result just given about integrating a power series term by term is all that we can obtain from a straightforward application of Theorem 31 to the general case. If the series $\sum a_n x^n$ is one which is absolutely convergent when $|x| = R$, then

$$\int_0^x f(t)\, dt = \sum a_n \frac{x^{n+1}}{n+1} \quad \text{when } |x| \leqslant R,$$

since there is then uniform convergence in $(-R, R)$.

But by far the most useful result about the integration of power series is contained in Theorem 46, which follows. Its proof uses most of the facts we have proved concerning power series.

THEOREM 46. *If $f(t)$ denotes the sum of the series $\sum a_n t^n$, then*

$$\int_0^\alpha f(t)\, dt = \sum a_n \frac{\alpha^{n+1}}{n+1}$$

provided only that the latter series is convergent.

We shall first prove that

$$\int_0^1 \left(\sum_{n=0}^\infty b_n x^n \right) dx = \sum_{n=0}^\infty \frac{b_n}{n+1}$$

whenever the series on the right is convergent.

If $\sum b_n/(n+1)$ is convergent, then, by Theorem 43,

$$\sum |b_n x^n/(n+1)|$$

converges when $|x| < 1$. Hence, by Theorem 44, $\sum b_n x^n$ converges absolutely when $|x| < 1$ and, by Theorem 45, it converges uniformly with respect to x in $(0, \delta)$, where δ is any fixed positive number less than 1.

Let $\phi(x)$ denote the sum of $\sum b_n x^n$ when $|x| < 1$, and let δ be any number between 0 and 1. Then, on integrating a uniformly convergent series,

$$\int_0^\delta \phi(x)\, dx = \sum_{n=0}^\infty \frac{b_n \delta^{n+1}}{n+1}. \tag{1}$$

But, whether $\phi(x)$ remains finite or does not remain finite as $x \to 1$,

$$\int_0^1 \phi(x)\, dx = \lim \int_0^\delta \phi(x)\, dx \qquad (2)$$

as $\delta \to 1$ from values less than 1.

Also, by Theorem 29, whenever $\sum b_n/(n+1)$ is convergent we have

$$\sum_{n=0}^\infty \frac{b_n}{n+1} = \lim \sum_{n=0}^\infty \frac{b_n\, \delta^{n+1}}{n+1} \qquad (3)$$

as $\delta \to 1$ from values less than 1.

By (1), the R.H.S. of (2) = the R.H.S. of (3) for every positive $\delta < 1$. Hence they have the same limit as $\delta \to 1$, and

$$\int_0^1 \left(\sum_{n=0}^\infty b_n x^n \right) dx = \sum_{n=0}^\infty \frac{b_n}{n+1}$$

whenever the latter series is convergent.

Now put $b_n = a_n \alpha^{n+1}$ and, in the integral, $x = t/\alpha$; we get

$$\int_0^\alpha \left(\sum_{n=0}^\infty a_n \alpha^{n+1} \frac{t^n}{\alpha^n} \right) \frac{dt}{\alpha} = \sum_{n=0}^\infty \frac{a_n \alpha^{n+1}}{n+1}$$

provided only that the latter series is convergent. The theorem follows on simplifying the L.H.S. of the last equation.

2.7. We conclude with a theorem which justifies the device usually known as 'equating coefficients'.

THEOREM 47. *If one and the same function $f(x)$ can be expanded in a power series in two distinct ways, so that*

$$f(x) = \sum_{n=0}^\infty a_n x^n = \sum_{n=0}^\infty b_n x^n,$$

both series being convergent when $|x| < R$, then $a_n = b_n$ for all values of n.

If we write $a_n - b_n = c_n$, then, when $|x| < R$,

$$0 = \sum_{n=0}^\infty c_n x^n, \qquad (1)$$

and our theorem is equivalent to saying that a power series cannot represent zero unless all its coefficients are zero.

Let R_1 be any positive number less than R. Then, by

Theorem 45, $\sum c_n x^n$ is uniformly convergent in $(-R_1, R_1)$ and so, by Theorem 32, its sum is a continuous function of x in $(-R_1, R_1)$. Hence, if $\phi(x)$ denotes its sum,

$$c_0 = \phi(0) = \lim_{x \to 0} \phi(x) = \lim_{x \to 0} 0 = 0.$$

Hence c_0 is zero; when $x \neq 0$ we have, on dividing (1) by x,

$$0 = \sum_{n=1}^{\infty} c_n x^{n-1} \quad (|x| < R, \ x \neq 0). \tag{2}$$

If $\psi(x)$ denotes $\sum c_n x^{n-1}$, the previous argument gives

$$c_1 = \psi(0) = \lim_{x \to 0} \psi(x).$$

But, by (2), $\psi(x) = 0$ when $x \neq 0$, and therefore the limit of $\psi(x)$ as x *tends* to zero is also 0. Hence $c_1 = 0$, and so on for the coefficients $c_2, c_3, \ldots, c_n, \ldots$.

3. The behaviour of a power series on its circle of convergence

In all the preceding discussion we have considered the question of convergence for points z that lie on the circle of convergence, $|z| = R$, only in the very easy case when $\sum |a_n| R^n$ is convergent. Then, of course, $\sum a_n z^n$ is convergent when $|z| = R$.

If $\sum |a_n| R^n$ is not convergent, then almost anything may happen to the series $\sum a_n z^n$ when $|z| = R$. There are series that converge, but not absolutely, for all z whose modulus is R; there are series that do not converge at all. As an example of the latter take $\sum z^n$. Its sum to n terms when $z = \cos \theta + i \sin \theta$ is given by

$$1 + z + \ldots + z^{n-1} = (1 - z^n)/(1 - z)$$
$$= \frac{1 - \cos n\theta - i \sin n\theta}{1 - \cos \theta - i \sin \theta}$$
$$= \frac{\sin \frac{1}{2} n\theta}{\sin \frac{1}{2}\theta} \left\{ \cos \frac{n-1}{2}\theta + i \sin \frac{n-1}{2}\theta \right\},$$

and, θ being fixed, this does not tend to a definite limit as n tends to infinity.

Again, there are series that converge at all points save one of their circle of convergence, some at all points save two, and so on. For example

$$1+z+\frac{z^2}{2}+\dots+\frac{z^n}{n}+\dots$$

has $|z| = 1$ for its circle of convergence. It does not converge when $z = 1$. But, when $z = \cos\theta+i\sin\theta$ and $0 < \theta < 2\pi$, each of the series

$$\sum \frac{\cos n\theta}{n}, \qquad \sum \frac{\sin n\theta}{n}$$

is convergent (Chap. IX, §3.5). That is, the series $\sum z^n/n$ converges at all points save one of its circle of convergence.

EXAMPLES XVIII

1. If $\sum a_n$ is convergent, then $\sum a_n x^n$ is uniformly convergent in $(0, 1)$ (Examples XVI, 7), and if $\sum (-1)^n a_n$ is convergent, then $\sum a_n x^n$ is uniformly convergent in $(-1, 0)$.

2. If $f(x) = \sum a_n x^n$ when $|x| < R_1$, and if $g(x) = \sum b_n x^n$ when $|x| < R_2$, then $f(x)g(x) = \sum c_n x^n$, where

$$c_n = a_0 b_n+a_1 b_{n-1}+\dots+a_n b_0, \quad \text{when } |x| < R_1, R_2.$$

3. Differentiate $\quad \left\{1+x+\frac{x^2}{2!}+\dots+\frac{x^{n-1}}{(n-1)!}\right\}e^{-x}$

and hence prove that its expansion is

$$1-\frac{x^n}{(n-1)!}\left\{\frac{1}{n}-\frac{x}{n+1}+\frac{x^2}{2!(n+2)}-\dots\right\}.$$

4. Determine the radius of convergence of each of the series

$$\sum nz^n, \qquad \sum \frac{n+1}{(n+2)(n+3)}z^n, \qquad \sum n^2z^n, \qquad \sum \frac{nz^n}{(n+1)^2}$$

and find the sum of each series. (The ratio tests for absolute convergence give unity as radius of convergence.) Show that the second and fourth series converge when $z = -1$.

5. Prove that $\quad 1+\frac{a.b}{1.c}z+\frac{a(a+1)b(b+1)}{1.2.c(c+1)}z^2+\dots$

has unit radius of convergence.

6. If $F(a,b;c;z)$ denotes the sum of the series in Example 5, prove that

(i) $\dfrac{d}{dz}F(a,b;c;z) = \dfrac{ab}{c}F(a+1,b+1;c+1;z);$

(ii) $F(a,b;c;z) = (1-z)^{c-a-b}F(c-b,c-a;c;z).$

7. By considering the coefficient of x^{n-1} in the expansion of $(1-x-x^2)^{-1}$, prove that

$$1+(n-2)+\frac{(n-3)(n-4)}{2!}+... = \frac{\alpha^n-\beta^n}{\alpha-\beta},$$

where α, β are the roots of the equation $u^2-u-1 = 0$.

8. Prove that if $(a_0+a_1x+...+a_kx^k)^{-1} = \sum p_nx^n$ when $|x|$ is sufficiently small, then

$$a_0p_n+a_1p_{n-1}+...+a_kp_{n-k} = 0 \quad (n \geqslant 1)$$

provided that $p_{-1}, p_{-2},...$ are interpreted to be zero.

9. Prove that each of the series

$$-1+\frac{2x^3}{2.3}+\frac{2.5.8.x^6}{2.3.5.6} +...,$$

$$x+\frac{4x^4}{3.4}+\frac{4.7.10.x^7}{3.4.6.7} +...$$

is convergent when $|4x^3| < 1$. If y denotes the sum of either series, then

$$(4x^3-1)\frac{d^2y}{dx^2}+6x^2\frac{dy}{dx}-2xy = 0.$$

10. (*Harder.*) By considering the expansion of

$$x^m(x+1)^m(2x+1)-x^m(x-1)^m(2x-1)$$

in powers of x, determine s_2 and s_4 when $s_r = 1^r+2^r+...+n^r$, and show that s_{2m}, where m is a positive integer, is equal to $n(n+1)(2n+1)$ multiplied by a polynomial in $n(n+1)$.

11. Prove that the series

$$\frac{1}{2}\frac{x^3}{3}+\frac{1}{2.4}\frac{x^5}{5}+\frac{1.3}{2.4.6}\frac{x^7}{7}+...$$

is convergent (i) when $0 < x < 1$, (ii) when $x = 1$.

Find, in each case, the sum of the series.

12. Prove that the series

$$x+\frac{x^2}{2^2}+\frac{2!}{3^3}x^3+\frac{3!}{4^4}x^4+...$$

converges if $|x| < e$.

13. Show that

$$1-\frac{1}{5}+\frac{1}{9}-\frac{1}{13}+\frac{1}{17}-... = \frac{\pi}{4\sqrt{2}}+\frac{1}{2\sqrt{2}}\log(1+\sqrt{2}).$$

14. Prove that the radius of convergence of the series

$$\frac{1}{2}x+\frac{1.3}{2.5}x^2+\frac{1.3.5}{2.5.8}x^3+...$$

is $\frac{3}{2}$.

15. Prove that the series $1+A_1z+A_2z^2+...$, where

$$A_n = q^{\frac{1}{2}n(n+1)}/(q-1)(q^2-1)...(q^n-1)$$

and $|q| < 1$, converges for all values of z. If $F(z)$ is the sum of the series, prove that $F(z) = (1-qz)F(qz)$.

Find the value of B_n if

$$\{F(z)\}^{-1} = 1 + B_1 z + \ldots + B_n z^n + \ldots$$

and prove that this series converges when $|zq| < 1$.

16. Prove that, if $F(a, b; c; z)$ is the sum of series in Example 5, then

$$z(1-z)\frac{d^2F}{dz^2} + \{c - (a+b+1)z\}\frac{dF}{dz} - abF = 0,$$

$$F(a, b; c; z) - F(a, b; c-1; z) = -\frac{abz}{c(c-1)} F(a+1, b+1; c+1; z).$$

CHAPTER XIV

THE INTEGRAL TEST

1. The integral test for series of positive terms

1.1. THEOREM 48. *If $f(x) > 0$ when $x > 0$, and if $f(x)$ decreases as x increases, then the sequences*

$$s_n \equiv f(1) + f(2) + \ldots + f(n) \quad (n = 1, 2, \ldots),$$

$$I_n \equiv \int_1^n f(x)\, dx \qquad (n = 1, 2, \ldots)$$

are either both convergent or both divergent.

Since $f(x) > 0$ when $x > 0$, the sequence (s_n) is monotonic increasing and the sequence (I_n) is monotonic increasing.

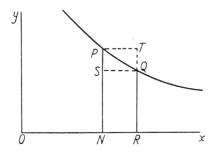

Let P, Q be points on the graph $y = f(x)$ such that $x = n$, $n+1$ respectively. Then, from the graph,

rect. $NRQS <$ area $NRQP <$ rect. $NRTP$.

Hence, since $NR = 1$, $NP = f(n)$, $RQ = f(n+1)$,

$$f(n+1) < \int_n^{n+1} f(x)\, dx < f(n). \tag{1}$$

If we write down (1) with the special values $n = 1, 2, \ldots, n-1$, and add, we have

$$s_n - f(1) < I_n < s_n - f(n). \tag{2}$$

Now suppose that $I_n \to$ a finite limit I as $n \to \infty$. Since (I_n) is m.i., we have $I_n \leqslant I$, and so, from (2),

$$s_n < I_n + f(1) \leqslant I + f(1). \tag{3}$$

But $I+f(1)$ is independent of n, so that, by (3), (s_n) is a m.i. sequence whose upper bound $\leqslant I+f(1)$. Hence $s_n \to$ a finite limit, s say, such that $s \leqslant I+f(1)$.

Similarly, if $s_n \to$ a finite limit s, (2) gives

$$I_n < s_n - f(n) < s_n \leqslant s$$

and $I_n \to I \leqslant s$.

If $I_n \to \infty$, then, since $s_n > I_n + f(n)$, $s_n \to \infty$; and if $s_n \to \infty$, then, since $I_n > s_n - f(1)$, $I_n \to \infty$.

NOTES. 1. A better proof of the last two lines is 'A m.i. sequence must converge or diverge: the convergence of either one of (s_n), (I_n) implies the convergence of the other; hence the divergence of either implies the divergence of the other'.

But not every one finds it easy to follow.

2. For readers whose knowledge of integral calculus is sufficiently advanced, (1) may be proved without any appeal to graphical considerations thus:

When $n \leqslant x \leqslant n+1, f(n) \geqslant f(x) \geqslant f(n+1)$, and

$$\int_n^{n+1} f(n)\,dx \geqslant \int_n^{n+1} f(x)\,dx \geqslant \int_n^{n+1} f(n+1)\,dx,$$

i.e.
$$f(n) \geqslant \int_n^{n+1} f(x)\,dx \geqslant f(n+1).$$

The $=$ sign covers the case when $f(x)$ remains constant from $x = n$ to $x = n+1$.

COROLLARY. $\sum n^{-p}$ *is convergent if* $p > 1$, *divergent if* $p \leqslant 1$.

For, when $f(n) = n^{-p}$,

$$I_n = \int_1^n \frac{dx}{x^p} = \frac{n^{1-p}-1}{1-p} \quad \text{or} \quad \log n,$$

according as $p \neq 1$ or $p = 1$.

1.2. There are numerous occasions when the comparison of a series with an integral is a useful step. Especially is this the case when the integral can be evaluated.

If $f(x)$ decreases as x increases we have, from (1),

$$f(n+1)+\ldots+f(n+k)$$
$$< \int_n^{n+k} f(x)\,dx < f(n)+\ldots+f(n+k-1) < \int_{n-1}^{n+k-1} f(x)\,dx.$$

For example, when n and k are integers,

$$\log\left(1+\frac{k}{n}\right) < \frac{1}{n}+\frac{1}{n+1}+...+\frac{1}{n+k-1} < \log\left(1+\frac{k}{n-1}\right),$$

$$\frac{k}{n(n+k)} < \frac{1}{n^2}+\frac{1}{(n+1)^2}+...+\frac{1}{(n+k-1)^2} < \frac{k}{(n-1)(n-1+k)},$$

$$\frac{1}{n^2+1}+\frac{1}{(n+1)^2+1}+...+\frac{1}{(n+k-1)^2+1}$$
$$< \tan^{-1}\left\{\frac{k}{(n-1)^2+k(n-1)+1}\right\}.$$

If we keep n fixed and let $k \to \infty$, we see from the second of these examples that

$$\frac{1}{n^2}+\frac{1}{(n+1)^2}+...$$

lies between $1/n$ and $1/(n-1)$.

2. Euler's constant

THEOREM 49. *If $f(x) > 0$ when $x > 0$, and if $f(x)$ decreases as x increases, then*

$$f(1)+f(2)+...+f(n)- \int_1^n f(x)\,dx \tag{4}$$

tends to a finite limit as $n \to \infty$.

Write ϕ_n to represent (4). Then, by (2),

$$\phi_n = s_n-I_n > f(n) > 0. \tag{5}$$

Further,

$$\phi_{n+1}-\phi_n = (s_{n+1}-s_n)-(I_{n+1}-I_n)$$
$$= f(n+1)- \int_n^{n+1} f(x)\,dx$$
$$< 0,$$

by (1). Hence

$$\phi_1 > \phi_2 > \phi_3 > ... > \phi_n > ... > 0; \tag{6}$$

that is, ϕ_n is a m.d. sequence whose lower bound $\geqslant 0$. Hence $\phi_n \to$ a finite limit.

COROLLARY. *In particular*

$$1+\frac{1}{2}+\dots+\frac{1}{n}-\int_{1}^{n}\frac{dx}{x},$$

that is,
$$1+\frac{1}{2}+\dots+\frac{1}{n}-\log n,$$

tends to a finite limit C, called Euler's constant.

The constant C (or, in an equally common notation, γ) is of frequent occurrence in analysis. The corollary itself expresses precisely what is often useful in the less precise form '$1+\frac{1}{2}+\dots+\frac{1}{n}$ is about as big as $\log n$'.

EXAMPLES XIX

1. Examples XIV, 1–6.

2. Prove by the integral test that the series $\sum\limits_{n=2}^{\infty} 1/n(\log n)^p$ is convergent if $p > 1$, divergent if $p \leqslant 1$. (Compare Theorem 17.)

3. Prove that if $p > 1$ the sum of the infinite series $1^{-p}+2^{-p}+\dots$ is less than $p/(p-1)$.

4. (*Harder.*) Prove that the series whose nth term is

$$\frac{1}{n}-\log\left(1+\frac{1}{n}\right)$$

is convergent, and that the sum of p terms of this series after the nth lies between

$$\frac{1}{2}\frac{p}{n(n+p)} \quad \text{and} \quad \frac{1}{2}\frac{p}{(n+1)(n+1+p)}\left(1-\frac{1}{3}\frac{2n+1+p}{n^2+np}\right).$$

[When $x > 0$, $\frac{1}{2}x^2-\frac{1}{3}x^3 < x-\log(1+x) < \frac{1}{2}x^2$.]

5. Find the limits as $n \to \infty$ of

$$\frac{1}{n+1}+\frac{1}{n+2}+\dots+\frac{1}{2n}, \qquad \frac{1}{n+1}-\frac{1}{n+2}+\dots+\frac{(-)^{n-1}}{2n}.$$

6. If x is real, show that

$$x^2+\left(1-\frac{1}{3}+\frac{1}{5}\right)\frac{x^6}{3}+\left(1-\frac{1}{3}+\frac{1}{5}-\frac{1}{7}+\frac{1}{9}\right)\frac{x^{10}}{5}+\dots$$

converges when $|x| < 1$ but not otherwise. Show that its sum is $(\tan^{-1}x)(\tanh^{-1}x)$.

7. Prove that, when $0 \geqslant p > -1$,

$$1^p+2^p+\dots+n^p-\frac{n^{p+1}}{p+1}$$

tends to a finite limit as $n \to \infty$, and hence that

$$\{(1^p+2^p+\dots+n^p)/n^{p+1}\} \to 1/(p+1).$$

CHAPTER XV

THE ORDER NOTATION

1. Gauss's ratio test

1.1. If $\sum u_n$ is a series of *positive* terms, and if the ratio (u_n/u_{n+1}) tends to a limit other than unity, then Theorem 10 decides at once whether the series is convergent or divergent. For a large number of series whose terms are such that (u_n/u_{n+1}) tends to unity, the following theorem will decide whether the series is convergent or divergent.

THEOREM 50. *If u_n is real, and if the ratio (u_n/u_{n+1}) can, when $n \geqslant$ some fixed N, be expressed in the form*

$$\frac{u_n}{u_{n+1}} = 1 + \frac{\mu}{n} + \frac{A_n}{n^{\lambda+1}}, \tag{1}$$

where $|A_n| < a$ fixed number K, and $\lambda > 0$, then $\sum u_n$ is convergent when $\mu > 1$, divergent when $\mu \leqslant 1$.

We see at once that u_n is eventually of constant sign and that

$$n\left(\frac{u_n}{u_{n+1}} - 1\right) \to \mu \quad \text{as } n \to \infty,$$

and so (Theorem 11) the series converges when $\mu > 1$ and diverges when $\mu < 1$.

When $\mu = 1$ we apply Theorem 12 with $D_n = n \log n$; by Theorem 17, $\sum D_n^{-1}$ is then divergent. When $\mu = 1$ and $D_n = n \log n$,

$$D_n \frac{u_n}{u_{n+1}} - D_{n+1} = n \log n \left\{ 1 + \frac{1}{n} + \frac{A_n}{n^{1+\lambda}} \right\} - (n+1)\log(n+1)$$

$$= \frac{A_n \log n}{n^\lambda} - (n+1)\log\left(1 + \frac{1}{n}\right).$$

But, by Theorem 40, $n^{-\lambda} \log n \to 0$ when $\lambda > 0$, and so, since $|A_n|$ remains less than a fixed K, $A_n n^{-\lambda} \log n \to 0$ when $\lambda > 0$. Also (by Chap. XII, § 9 (2))

$$\frac{1}{n+1} < \log\left(1 + \frac{1}{n}\right) < \frac{1}{n},$$

so that $(n+1)\log\left(1+\dfrac{1}{n}\right) \to 1$. Hence

$$D_n\frac{u_n}{u_{n+1}} - D_{n+1} \to -1,$$

and $\sum u_n$ is divergent when $\mu = 1$.

1.2. In many examples it is not difficult to see that the ratio (u_n/u_{n+1}) can be expressed in the form (1). Consider the series

$$\frac{1}{x} + \frac{2!}{x(x+1)} + \frac{3!}{x(x+1)(x+2)} + \cdots. \qquad (2)$$

Here

$$\frac{u_n}{u_{n+1}} = \frac{x+n}{n+1} = 1 + \frac{x-1}{n+1}$$

$$= 1 + \frac{x-1}{n} - \frac{x-1}{n(n+1)},$$

and if we write

$$-\frac{x-1}{n(n+1)} = \frac{A_n}{n^2},$$

then $|A_n| < |x-1|$. Hence if x is fixed, the ratio (u_n/u_{n+1}) can be expressed in the form (1) with $\mu = x-1$, and the series (2) converges when $x-1 > 1$, diverges when $x-1 \leqslant 1$.

1.3. The test contained in Theorem 50 becomes more powerful when it is combined with the technique of using the order notation, which we shall now explain.

2. The order notation

2.1. Let $f(n)$ be a given function of n, a variable positive integer. If the sequence $\{f(n)/n^r\}$ is bounded, that is, if there is a number K such that

$$\left|\frac{f(n)}{n^r}\right| < K \quad \text{or, what is the same,} \quad |f(n)| < Kn^r \qquad (3)$$

for all n, we write $f(n) = O(n^r)$. If (3) holds when $r = 0$, that is, if the sequence $\{f(n)\}$ is bounded, we write $f(n) = O(1)$.

EXAMPLES.

(i) $(n+2)^2 = O(n^2)$.

For $\dfrac{(n+2)^2}{n^2} = 1 + \dfrac{4}{n} + \dfrac{4}{n^2} \to 1 \quad \text{as } n \to \infty.$

By Theorem 1, a convergent sequence is bounded, and so the sequence $\{(n+2)^2/n^2\}$ is bounded.

(ii) $(n^3+n)^{-\frac{1}{2}} = O(n^{-\frac{3}{2}})$.

For
$$\left| \frac{1}{\sqrt{(n^3+n)}} \right| < \frac{1}{\sqrt{n^3}} = n^{-\frac{3}{2}}.$$

(iii) $\dfrac{3n-4}{n+3} = O(1)$.

For the sequence $\dfrac{3n-4}{n+3} \to 3$ and so, by Theorem 1, is bounded.

2.2. Sometimes the function $f(n)$ is comparable to some function other than a power of n. For example, the notations

$$f(n) = O(e^{2n}), \qquad f(n) = O(n \log 2n)$$

mean respectively that

$$\frac{f(n)}{e^{2n}}, \qquad \frac{f(n)}{n \log 2n} \qquad (n = 1, 2, \ldots)$$

are bounded sequences.

Sometimes, too, n must be restricted if the relation implied by the O symbol is to be true. Thus

$$\frac{1}{n-1} = O\!\left(\frac{1}{n}\right) \quad \text{when } n \geqslant 2.$$

For
$$\frac{1}{n-1} \div \frac{1}{n} = \frac{n}{n-1},$$

which takes the values $2, \frac{3}{2}, \ldots$ when $n = 2, 3$, and each of these values $\leqslant 2$: but we cannot admit the value $n = 1$.

Similarly,

$$\frac{1}{(n-a)(n-b)} = O\!\left(\frac{1}{n^2}\right) \quad \text{when } n \geqslant N > a, b,$$

and, more generally,

$$\frac{a_0 n^p + a_1 n^{p-1} + \ldots + a_p}{b_0 n^q + b_1 n^{q-1} + \ldots + b_q} = O(n^{p-q}) \quad \text{when } n \geqslant N,$$

where N is greater than every real root of the equation

$$b_0 x^q + \ldots + b_q = 0.$$

2.3. When one is thoroughly practised in the use of the O notation, it is convenient to modify it. Usually, one is not interested in the behaviour of $f(n)$ save when $n \to \infty$, and the limitations $n \geqslant 1$, $n \geqslant N$

are merely irksome details without real relevance to the problem in hand. The common practice is to write

$$f(n) = O(n^{-2})$$

to mean that 'if we fix n_0 suitably, there is a constant K such that

$$|f(n)| < Kn^{-2} \quad \text{when } n \geqslant n_0\text{'}.$$

This practice is recommended to the reader only after he has worked for some time with the notation in which the limitations $n \geqslant 1$, $n \geqslant |a|$, etc., are taken into account.

3. The limit notation

In much the same way the notations

$$f(n) = o(n), \qquad f(n) = o(n^{-3})$$

denote respectively the facts that

$$\frac{f(n)}{n} \to 0, \qquad n^3 f(n) \to 0 \quad \text{as } n \to \infty,$$

while the notation $\qquad f(n) = o(1)$

denotes that $\qquad f(n) \to 0 \quad \text{as } n \to \infty.$

4. Applications of the order notation

4.1. THEOREM 51. *If, for $n \geqslant 1$,*

$$f(n) = \alpha_0 + \frac{\alpha_1}{n} + \frac{\alpha_2}{n^2} + \cdots,$$

where the α's are independent of n and the series is absolutely convergent when $n = 1$, then

$$f(n) = \alpha_0 + O\left(\frac{1}{n}\right),$$

$$f(n) = \alpha_0 + \frac{\alpha_1}{n} + O\left(\frac{1}{n^2}\right),$$

and so on.

By hypothesis, $\sum |\alpha_r|$ is convergent, and so the series

$$\alpha_1 + \alpha_2 x + \alpha_3 x^2 + \cdots$$

converges uniformly in $|x| \leqslant 1$. Hence its sum is a continuous function of x in $|x| \leqslant 1$. In particular, its sum $\to \alpha_1$ as $x \to 0$. Hence the sequence

$$n\{f(n) - \alpha_0\} \quad (n = 1, 2, 3, \ldots)$$

tends to the finite limit α_1 as $n \to \infty$. Accordingly, this sequence is bounded and there is a K such that

$$n|f(n)-\alpha_0| < K,$$

i.e.
$$f(n)-\alpha_0 = O\!\left(\frac{1}{n}\right).$$

In order to prove that

$$f(n)-\alpha_0-\frac{\alpha_1}{n} = O\!\left(\frac{1}{n^2}\right)$$

we repeat the same argument, beginning now with the series $\alpha_2+\alpha_3 x+\dots$.

COROLLARY. *If* $f(n) = \alpha_0+\alpha_1 n^{-1}+\alpha_2 n^{-2}+\dots$ *is absolutely convergent only when* $n \geqslant$ *some fixed* N, *then*

$$f(n) = \alpha_0+O(n^{-1}), \qquad f(n) = \alpha_0+\alpha_1 n^{-1}+O(n^{-2}) \quad when \ n \geqslant N,$$

and so on.

In this case the sequence

$$n\{f(n)-\alpha_0\} \quad (n = N, N+1,\dots)$$

is bounded.

EXAMPLES.

(i) $\quad \left(1+\dfrac{1}{n}\right)^k = 1+\dfrac{k}{n}+O\!\left(\dfrac{1}{n^2}\right) \quad$ when $n \geqslant 2$,

(ii) $\quad \left(1+\dfrac{a}{n}\right)^k = 1+\dfrac{ka}{n}+O\!\left(\dfrac{1}{n^2}\right) \quad$ when $n \geqslant N > |a|$,

(iii) $\quad \log\!\left(1+\dfrac{1}{n}\right) = \dfrac{1}{n}+O\!\left(\dfrac{1}{n^2}\right) \quad$ when $n \geqslant 2$,

(iv) $\qquad\quad e^{a/n} = 1+\dfrac{a}{n}+O\!\left(\dfrac{1}{n^2}\right).$

In (i) our method gives the result when $n \geqslant 2$ and not when $n \geqslant 1$ because, unless $k+1 > 0$, the binomial series does not converge when $n = 1$.

4.2. THEOREM 52. *If* a, b *are fixed, and if*

$$f(n) = 1+\frac{a}{n}+O\!\left(\frac{1}{n^2}\right), \qquad \phi(n) = 1+\frac{b}{n}+O\!\left(\frac{1}{n^2}\right) \quad when \ n \geqslant N,$$

then $\qquad f(n)\phi(n) = 1+\dfrac{a+b}{n}+O\!\left(\dfrac{1}{n^2}\right) \quad when \ n \geqslant N.$

By hypothesis, when $n \geqslant N$,

$$f(n) = 1 + \frac{a}{n} + \frac{A_n}{n^2}, \qquad \phi(n) = 1 + \frac{b}{n} + \frac{B_n}{n^2},$$

where $|A_n| < K_1$ and $|B_n| < K_2$. Hence

$$f(n)\phi(n) - 1 - \frac{a+b}{n} = \frac{1}{n^2}\left\{ ab + A_n\left(1 + \frac{b}{n}\right) + B_n\left(1 + \frac{a}{n}\right) \right\}.$$

Moreover, the sequences

$$1 + \frac{b}{n}, \qquad 1 + \frac{a}{n} \qquad (n = N, N+1, \dots)$$

are convergent and so there are constants, K_3 and K_4 say, such that

$$\left| 1 + \frac{b}{n} \right| < K_3, \qquad \left| 1 + \frac{a}{n} \right| < K_4 \qquad (n \geqslant N).$$

Hence, when $n \geqslant N$,

$$\left| f(n)\phi(n) - 1 - \frac{a+b}{n} \right| \leqslant \frac{1}{n^2}\{ |ab| + K_1 K_3 + K_2 K_4 \},$$

and the latter is a constant multiple of $(1/n^2)$.

4.3. The result of Theorem 52 may be written

$$\left\{ 1 + \frac{a}{n} + O\left(\frac{1}{n^2}\right) \right\}\left\{ 1 + \frac{b}{n} + O\left(\frac{1}{n^2}\right) \right\} \quad (n \geqslant N)$$

$$= 1 + \frac{a+b}{n} + O\left(\frac{1}{n^2}\right) \quad (n \geqslant N).$$

It includes as a special case ($A_n = 0$ in § 4.2)

$$\left(1 + \frac{a}{n} \right)\left\{ 1 + \frac{b}{n} + O\left(\frac{1}{n^2}\right) \right\} \quad (n \geqslant N)$$

$$= 1 + \frac{a+b}{n} + O\left(\frac{1}{n^2}\right) \quad (n \geqslant N).$$

4.4. Applications to Theorem 50.

(i) The series

$$\frac{1}{x} + \frac{2!}{x(x+1)} + \frac{3!}{x(x+1)(x+2)} + \dots$$

is convergent when $x-1 > 1$, divergent when $x-1 \leqslant 1$.

$$\frac{u_n}{u_{n+1}} = \frac{n+x}{n+1} = \left(1+\frac{x}{n}\right)\left(1+\frac{1}{n}\right)^{-1}$$

$$= \left(1+\frac{x}{n}\right)\left\{1-\frac{1}{n}+O\left(\frac{1}{n^2}\right)\right\} \quad (n \geqslant 2)$$

$$= 1+\frac{x-1}{n}+O\left(\frac{1}{n^2}\right),$$

and Theorem 50 proves the result.

Or the work may be set out as in § 1.2.

(ii) The series $\sum\left(\dfrac{2.4...2n}{3.5...2n+1}\right)^2$ is divergent.

$$\frac{u_n}{u_{n+1}} = \left(\frac{2n+3}{2n+2}\right)^2 = \left(1+\frac{3}{2n}\right)^2\left(1+\frac{1}{n}\right)^{-2}$$

$$= \left\{1+\frac{3}{n}+O\left(\frac{1}{n^2}\right)\right\}\left\{1-\frac{2}{n}+O\left(\frac{1}{n^2}\right)\right\} \quad (n \geqslant 2)$$

$$= 1+\frac{1}{n}+O\left(\frac{1}{n^2}\right),$$

and the divergence of $\sum u_n$ is proved by Theorem 50.

Or, on the lines of § 1.2,

$$\left(\frac{2n+3}{2n+2}\right)^2 = \left(1+\frac{1}{2n+2}\right)^2 = 1+\frac{1}{n+1}+\frac{1}{4(n+1)^2},$$

and, if we write this as

$$1+\frac{1}{n}+\frac{A_n}{n^2},$$

then

$$\frac{A_n}{n^2} = \frac{1}{n+1}-\frac{1}{n}+\frac{1}{4(n+1)^2}$$

$$= \frac{1}{4(n+1)^2}-\frac{1}{n(n+1)},$$

$$|A_n| \leqslant n^2\left\{\frac{1}{4n^2}+\frac{1}{n^2}\right\} = \frac{5}{4},$$

and the divergence of $\sum u_n$ is proved by Theorem 50.

5. Series of complex terms

Let $u_n = v_n + iw_n$, and let

$$\frac{u_n}{u_{n+1}} = 1 + \frac{\alpha + i\beta}{n} + \frac{A_n + iB_n}{n^2}, \tag{1}$$

where $|A_n|$, $|B_n|$ are bounded for all $n \geqslant$ some fixed N.

If we recall the fact that, when $z = x + iy$,

$$|z|^2 = (x+iy)(x-iy),$$

we see that (1) gives (on using Theorem 52 extended to complex† a, b)

$$\left| \frac{u_n}{u_{n+1}} \right|^2 = \left\{ 1 + \frac{\alpha + i\beta}{n} + O\!\left(\frac{1}{n^2}\right) \right\} \left\{ 1 + \frac{\alpha - i\beta}{n} + O\!\left(\frac{1}{n^2}\right) \right\}$$

$$= 1 + \frac{2\alpha}{n} + O\!\left(\frac{1}{n^2}\right),$$

and so, by the binomial expansion for $(1+x)^{\frac{1}{2}}$,

$$\left| \frac{u_n}{u_{n+1}} \right| = 1 + \frac{\alpha}{n} + O\!\left(\frac{1}{n^2}\right). \tag{2}$$

Hence if the terms of a series $\sum u_n$ are such that (1) holds, then the series is absolutely convergent when $\alpha > 1$; that is, for absolute convergence, the real part of $\alpha + i\beta$ must exceed unity.

Examples XX

1. Prove that, when b is neither zero nor a negative integer,

$$\frac{a}{b} + \frac{a(a+1)}{b(b+1)} + \cdots$$

is absolutely convergent if $b - a > 1$.

2. Prove that the hypergeometric series

$$1 + \frac{\alpha \cdot \beta}{1 \cdot \gamma} x + \frac{\alpha(\alpha+1)\beta(\beta+1)}{1 \cdot 2 \cdot \gamma(\gamma+1)} x^2 + \cdots$$

has unit radius of convergence and converges absolutely when $|x| = 1$ if (i) $\gamma > \alpha + \beta$, or (ii), assuming α, β, γ to be complex, if the real part of $\gamma - \alpha - \beta$ is positive.

† The only new fact wanted is 'if $a_n = \alpha_n + i\beta_n$ is a sequence that converges to a finite limit $\alpha + i\beta$, then $|a_n|$ is bounded'. This follows at once from Theorem 1: for $\alpha_n \to \alpha$, $\beta_n \to \beta$ and so $|\alpha_n|$, $|\beta_n|$ are bounded. Hence $|a_n| = \sqrt{(\alpha_n^2 + \beta_n^2)}$ is bounded.

3. Prove that, when a and b are positive,

$$\frac{a}{b} + \frac{a(2a+1)}{b(2b+1)} + \frac{a(2a+1)(3a+1)}{b(2b+1)(3b+1)} + \ldots$$

is convergent if and only if $b > a$ (Theorem 10).

4. Prove that the infinite series

$$1 + \mu^2 + \left\{\frac{\mu(\mu-1)}{2!}\right\}^2 + \left\{\frac{\mu(\mu-1)(\mu-2)}{3!}\right\}^2 + \ldots$$

is absolutely convergent if the real part of $\mu > -\frac{1}{2}$.

5. The sequence (a_n) is such that

$$\frac{a_{n+1}}{a_n} = an + b + O\left(\frac{1}{n}\right).$$

Prove that the series

$$\sum \frac{a_n}{x(x+1)\ldots(x+n)}$$

is absolutely convergent when $|a| < 1$ and also when $a = 1$ provided that $x > b$.

In the following examples use the O notation as explained in § 2.3.

6. Prove that, when $\lambda > 0$,

$$1 + \frac{\alpha}{n} + O\left(\frac{1}{n^{1+\lambda}}\right) = \left(1 + \frac{\alpha}{n}\right)\left\{1 + O\left(\frac{1}{n^{1+\lambda}}\right)\right\},$$

and hence that

$$\log\left\{1 + \frac{\alpha}{n} + O\left(\frac{1}{n^{1+\lambda}}\right)\right\} = \frac{\alpha}{n} + O\left(\frac{1}{n^{1+\mu}}\right),$$

where $\mu > 0$.

7. Prove that, when $\lambda > 0$,

$$\exp\left\{\frac{\alpha}{n} + O\left(\frac{1}{n^{1+\lambda}}\right)\right\} = 1 + \frac{\alpha}{n} + O\left(\frac{1}{n^{1+\nu}}\right),$$

where $\nu > 0$.

8. Use Example 6, part (i), to prove that

$$\left\{1 + \frac{\alpha}{n} + O\left(\frac{1}{n^{1+\lambda}}\right)\right\}^k = 1 + \frac{k\alpha}{n} + O\left(\frac{1}{n^{1+\theta}}\right),$$

where $\theta > 0$.

CHAPTER XVI

TANNERY'S THEOREM

1. Tannery's theorem

1.1. We first prove what is usually known as Tannery's theorem in a form that differs from the original form given by Tannery himself. The new form accentuates the relation of the theorem to the idea of uniform convergence.

THEOREM 53. *Let*

$$F(x) = \sum_{n=1}^{\infty} v_n(x),$$

the series being uniformly convergent with regard to x for all positive x. Further, for each fixed n, let

$$v_n(x) \to w_n \quad as \quad x \to \infty.$$

Then the series $\sum w_n$ is convergent and

$$F(x) \to \sum_{n=1}^{\infty} w_n \quad as \quad x \to \infty.$$

(i) We first prove that $\sum w_n$ converges.

By the uniform convergence of $\sum v_n(x)$ for all positive x,

$\epsilon, k > 0; \quad \exists \; N$. for all positive x

$$\left| \sum_{N+1}^{N+p} v_n(x) \right| < \epsilon k \quad \text{when } p = 1, 2, \dots .$$

As $x \to \infty$, $v_{N+1}(x) + \dots + v_{N+p}(x) \to w_{N+1} + \dots + w_{N+p}$. Hence

$$\left| \sum_{N+1}^{N+p} w_n \right| \leqslant \epsilon k \quad \text{when } p = 1, 2, \dots .$$

On taking $k = \frac{1}{2}$, we see that

$$\epsilon > 0; \quad \exists \; N \; . \; \left| \sum_{N+1}^{N+p} w_n \right| < \epsilon \quad \text{when } p = 1, 2, \dots,$$

which is the condition that $\sum w_n$ should converge.

(ii) The convergence of $\sum w_n$ having been established, we make a fresh start. Let $W = \sum w_n$. Then, since $\sum v_n(x)$ converges uniformly to its sum $F(x)$ for all positive x, and since $\sum w_n$ converges to the sum W,

$$\epsilon, k > 0; \quad \exists \; N \; . \; \left| F(x) - \sum_{n=1}^{N} v_n(x) \right| < \epsilon k \quad \text{for all positive } x,$$

and
$$\left| W - \sum_{n=1}^{N} w_n \right| < \epsilon k.$$

Hence, for all positive x,

$$|F(x) - W| \leqslant \left| F(x) - \sum_{n=1}^{N} v_n(x) \right| + \left| \sum_{n=1}^{N} v_n(x) - \sum_{n=1}^{N} w_n \right| + \left| \sum_{n=1}^{N} w_n - W \right|$$

$$< 2\epsilon k + \left| \sum_{n=1}^{N} v_n(x) - \sum_{n=1}^{N} w_n \right|.$$

But as $x \to \infty$, each $v_n(x) \to w_n$ and so, since N is finite,

$$\sum_{n=1}^{N} v_n(x) \to \sum_{n=1}^{N} w_n.$$

Hence $\exists\ X$. $\left| \sum_{n=1}^{N} v_n(x) - \sum_{n=1}^{N} w_n \right| < \epsilon k$ when $x > X$.

Finally, then, we have $|F(x) - W| < 3\epsilon k$ when $x > X$. Hence, on taking $k = \frac{1}{3}$, we have proved that

$$\epsilon > 0;\ \ \exists\ X\ .\ |F(x) - W| < \epsilon\ \ \text{when } x > X,$$

which is the condition that $F(x) \to W$ as $x \to \infty$.

NOTE. The result is unaltered if there is uniform convergence, not for all positive x, but only for $x \geqslant X_1$, a fixed constant.

1.2. There is a particular case of Theorem 53 corresponding to each of the tests for uniform convergence established in Chapter XI, § 5. We shall enunciate two such particular cases.

THEOREM 54. *Let*

$$F(x) = \sum_{n=1}^{\infty} v_n(x),$$

and let $\sum M_n$ *be a convergent series of positive constants such that* $|v_n(x)| \leqslant M_n$ *for all positive x. Further, for each fixed n, let*

$$v_n(x) \to w_n \quad \text{as } x \to \infty.$$

Then the series $\sum w_n$ *is convergent and*

$$F(x) \to \sum_{n=1}^{\infty} w_n \quad \text{as } x \to \infty.$$

By an easy extension of Theorem 35, since $\sum M_n$ is convergent and $|v_n(x)| < M_n$ for all positive x, the series $\sum v_n(x)$ is uniformly convergent for all positive x.

THEOREM 55. *Let*

$$F(x) = \sum_{n=1}^{\infty} a_n v_n(x),$$

where $\sum a_n$ *is a convergent series of constants. Let* $v_n(x)$ *be monotonic decreasing (increasing) for each fixed x that is positive and let* $|v_n(x)| < K$ *for all n and for all positive x. Further, for each fixed n, let*

$$v_n(x) \to 1 \quad as \ x \to \infty.$$

Then $F(x) \to \sum a_n$ *as* $x \to \infty$.

By an easy extension of Theorem 37, $\sum a_n v_n(x)$ is uniformly convergent for all positive x. Further, $a_n v_n(x) \to a_n$ as $x \to \infty$, and so, by Theorem 53, $F(x) \to \sum a_n$.

1.3. Tannery's original theorem is a particular case of Theorem 54. If $v_n(x)$ has zero values when $n > k(x)$ we have the following result.

THEOREM 56. **Tannery's theorem.** *Let*

$$F(x) = \sum_{n=1}^{k(x)} v_n(x),$$

where

(i) $k(x) \to \infty$ *as* $x \to \infty$,

(ii) $|v_n(x)| \leqslant M_n$ *for all x, where M_n is independent of x, and $\sum M_n$ is convergent,*

(iii) *for each fixed n, $v_n(x) \to w_n$ as $x \to \infty$.*

Then $\qquad F(x) \to \sum w_n \quad$ *as* $x \to \infty$.

There is a corresponding particular case of Theorem 55 in which the value of $v_n(x)$ is zero when n exceeds $k(x)$.

2. Examples of Tannery's theorem

(i) $\qquad \left(1 + \frac{1}{n}\right)^n \to e \quad$ as $n \to \infty$.

If we write $F(n) = \{1 + (1/n)\}^n$, then, n being a positive integer, the elementary form of the binomial theorem gives

$$F(n) = 1 + n \cdot \frac{1}{n} + \frac{n(n-1)}{2!} \frac{1}{n^2} + \dots \quad \text{to } n+1 \text{ terms}$$

$$= 1 + 1 + \frac{1}{2!}\left(1 - \frac{1}{n}\right) + \frac{1}{3!}\left(1 - \frac{1}{n}\right)\left(1 - \frac{2}{n}\right) + \dots \quad \text{to } n+1 \text{ terms}.$$

Put $$v_r(n) = \frac{1}{r!}\left(1 - \frac{1}{n}\right)\cdots\left(1 - \frac{r-1}{n}\right).$$

Then, for each fixed $r \geqslant 2$,

$$|v_r(n)| < \frac{1}{r!} \quad \text{for all } n$$

and $$v_r(n) \to \frac{1}{r!} \quad \text{as } n \to \infty.$$

Moreover, $\sum (1/r!)$ is convergent. Hence, by Theorem 56,

$$F(n) \to 1 + 1 + \frac{1}{2!} + \frac{1}{3!} + \cdots + \frac{1}{r!} + \cdots.$$

(ii) If $x \to \infty$, not necessarily through integer values,

$$\left(1 + \frac{1}{x}\right)^x \to e.$$

The binomial theorem for any index shows that

$$\left(1 + \frac{1}{x}\right)^x = 1 + 1 + \frac{x(x-1)}{2!}\frac{1}{x^2} + \cdots$$

whenever $x > 1$. But, when x is positive,

$$|v_n(x)| \equiv \left|\frac{x(x-1)\dots(x-n+1)}{n!}\frac{1}{x^n}\right|$$
$$< \left|\frac{x(x+1)\dots(x+n-1)}{n!}\frac{1}{x^n}\right|.$$

If we write u_n to denote this last expression, then

$$\frac{u_n}{u_{n+1}} = \frac{(n+1)x}{x+n} = \frac{1+n}{1+n/x}.$$

When $x \geqslant 2$, $$\frac{u_n}{u_{n+1}} \geqslant \frac{1+n}{1+\frac{1}{2}n} = 1 + \frac{\frac{1}{2}n}{1+\frac{1}{2}n},$$

and when $n \geqslant 2$ the last expression $\geqslant \frac{3}{2}$.

Hence $u_3 \leqslant \frac{2}{3}u_2$, $u_4 \leqslant (\frac{2}{3})^2 u_2$, and so on. Also, when $x \geqslant 2$,

$$u_2 = \frac{x(x+1)}{2x^2} = \frac{1}{2}\left(1 + \frac{1}{x}\right) \leqslant \frac{1}{2} \cdot \frac{3}{2} < \frac{3}{2}.$$

Hence $u_n < (\frac{2}{3})^{n-3}$ when $n \geqslant 2$, so that

$$|v_n(x)| < (\tfrac{2}{3})^{n-3} \quad \text{when } n \geqslant 2 \text{ and } x \geqslant 2.$$

It is now a fairly straightforward application of Theorem 54 to show that $\{1+(1/x)\}^x \to e$ as $x \to \infty$.

EXAMPLES XXI

1. Prove that, when a is a real number,

(i) $\left(1+\dfrac{a}{n}\right)^n \to e^a$ as $n \to \infty$,

(ii) $\left(1+\dfrac{a}{x}\right)^x \to e^a$ as $x \to \infty$.

2. Show that
$$F(n) = \frac{1}{n+1}+\frac{1}{n+2}+\ldots+\frac{1}{2n} > \frac{1}{2}$$
and hence that $F(n)$ cannot tend to zero as $n \to \infty$, although $(n+r)^{-1} \to 0$ for each fixed r as $n \to \infty$.

3. THEOREM 54. Prove that
$$\sum_{n=1}^{\infty} \frac{1}{n^2+n^4/x^2} \to \sum_{n=1}^{\infty} \frac{1}{n^2} \quad \text{as } x \to \infty.$$

4. THEOREM 55 (with $x \to 1+0$ instead of $x \to \infty$).
$$\sum_{n=1}^{\infty} (-1)^{n-1} n^{-x} \to \log 2 \quad \text{as } x \to 1+0.$$

5. THEOREM 55 (with some $v_n(x)$ zero). Prove that, as $k \to \infty$,
$$a_1+\frac{k-1}{k}\,a_2+\frac{k-2}{k}\,a_3+\ldots+\frac{1}{k}a_k$$
tends to $\sum a_n$ whenever the latter series is convergent.

Hence prove that
$$\frac{s_1+s_2+\ldots+s_n}{n} \to s \quad \text{whenever } s_n \to s.$$

6. THEOREM 55 (with some $v_n(x)$ zero). The limit as $n \to \infty$ of
$$\sum_{r=1}^{n} (-1)^r \frac{(n!)^2}{(n-r)!\,(n+r)!} \frac{a_r}{x-r}$$
is given by the sum of the infinite series
$$\sum_{r=1}^{\infty} (-1)^r \frac{a_r}{x-r}$$
whenever the latter series is convergent.

CHAPTER XVII

DOUBLE SERIES

1. Double series

1.1. Consider the doubly infinite array

$$
\begin{array}{cccccc}
a_{11} & a_{12} & \cdot & \cdot & \cdot & a_{1n} & \cdot & \cdot \\
a_{21} & a_{22} & \cdot & \cdot & \cdot & a_{2n} & \cdot & \cdot \\
& & \cdot & \cdot & \cdot & \cdot & \cdot & \cdot \\
a_{m1} & a_{m2} & \cdot & \cdot & \cdot & a_{mn} & \cdot & \cdot \\
& & \cdot & \cdot & \cdot & \cdot & \cdot & \cdot
\end{array}
$$

Suppose that, for each fixed m, the infinite series formed by the terms in the mth row, that is,

$$a_{m1} + a_{m2} + \ldots + a_{mn} + \ldots,$$

has a finite sum, R_m say. Suppose further that the infinite series
$$R_1 + R_2 + R_3 + \ldots + R_m + \ldots$$

has a finite sum, R say. Then R is called the *sum by rows* of the double series $\sum \sum a_{mn}$.

Similarly, if, for each fixed n (i.e. each column),

$$a_{1n} + a_{2n} + \ldots + a_{mn} + \ldots$$

has a finite sum C_n, and if
$$C = C_1 + C_2 + C_3 + \ldots + C_n + \ldots,$$

then C is called the *sum by columns*.

1.2. Let S_{mn} denote the sum of all terms that are to be found in the rectangle formed by the common part of the first m rows and the first n columns. If there is a number S such that

$$\epsilon > 0; \ \exists \ N \ . \ |S - S_{mn}| < \epsilon \quad \text{when } m, n \geqslant N,$$

then S is called the *sum by rectangles*, or simply the sum, of the double series.

1.3. Double limits. When we consider a doubly infinite set of numbers

$$\alpha_{\mu\nu} \quad (\mu = 1, 2, \ldots; \nu = 1, 2, \ldots),$$

it is fairly obvious from the definition of 'limit' that the two numbers

$$\lim_{\mu \to \infty} \left\{ \lim_{\nu \to \infty} a_{\mu\nu} \right\}, \qquad \lim_{\nu \to \infty} \left\{ \lim_{\mu \to \infty} a_{\mu\nu} \right\}$$

are not necessarily equal. It is easy to construct examples where the two numbers are equal and to construct examples where they are not equal. For example, if

$$\alpha_{\mu\nu} = \frac{(\nu+1)(\mu+1)}{(\nu+2)(\mu+2)},$$

then, for each fixed ν,

$$\lim_{\mu\to\infty} \alpha_{\mu\nu} = \frac{\nu+1}{\nu+2},$$

and so

$$\lim_{\nu\to\infty}\left\{\lim_{\mu\to\infty}\alpha_{\mu\nu}\right\} = \lim_{\nu\to\infty}\frac{\nu+1}{\nu+2} = 1;$$

and a similar calculation shows that

$$\lim_{\mu\to\infty}\left\{\lim_{\nu\to\infty}\alpha_{\mu\nu}\right\} = \lim_{\mu\to\infty}\frac{\mu+1}{\mu+2} = 1.$$

On the other hand, if

$$\alpha_{\mu\nu} = \frac{\mu-\nu}{\mu+\nu}\frac{\mu(\nu+1)}{\nu(\mu+1)},$$

then, for each fixed μ,

$$\lim_{\nu\to\infty}\alpha_{\mu\nu} = \frac{-\mu}{\mu+1},$$

and, for each fixed ν, $$\lim_{\mu\to\infty}\alpha_{\mu\nu} = \frac{\nu+1}{\nu}.$$

Hence

$$\lim_{\mu\to\infty}\left\{\lim_{\nu\to\infty}\alpha_{\mu\nu}\right\} = \lim_{\mu\to\infty}\frac{-\mu}{\mu+1} = -1,$$

and

$$\lim_{\nu\to\infty}\left\{\lim_{\mu\to\infty}\alpha_{\mu\nu}\right\} = \lim_{\nu\to\infty}\frac{\nu+1}{\nu} = 1.$$

Going back to the sum by rows and the sum by columns of § 1.1, we see that if

$$S_{\mu\nu} = \sum_{m=1}^{\mu}\sum_{n=1}^{\nu} a_{mn},$$

then

$$\lim_{\nu\to\infty} S_{\mu\nu} = \sum_{m=1}^{\mu} R_m,$$

and so

$$\lim_{\mu\to\infty}\left\{\lim_{\nu\to\infty} S_{\mu\nu}\right\} = \sum_{m=1}^{\infty} R_m = R,$$

the sum by rows.

Similarly, $$\lim_{\nu\to\infty}\left\{\lim_{\mu\to\infty} S_{\mu\nu}\right\} = \sum_{n=1}^{\infty} C_n = C,$$

the sum by columns.

As we have seen by examples, C and R need not be equal.

1.4. We shall not attempt a discussion of the general theory of double series. All we do here is to state simple conditions which will ensure that the sum by rows is equal to the sum by columns.

2. Double series of positive terms

THEOREM 57. *If each a_{mn} is positive or zero in the array*

$$
\begin{array}{cccccccc}
a_{11} & a_{12} & . & . & . & a_{1n} & . & . \\
a_{21} & a_{22} & . & . & . & a_{2n} & . & . \\
 & & . & . & . & . & . & . \\
a_{m1} & a_{m2} & . & . & . & a_{mn} & . & . \\
 & & . & . & . & . & . & .
\end{array}
$$

and if there is a finite sum by rows, then there is a finite sum by columns and the two sums are equal.

First step. We can arrange the terms of the array as terms in a single sequence in a number of different ways: for example, we can write a_{11}; then all terms the sum of whose suffixes is 3, namely a_{21} and a_{12}; then terms a_{31}, a_{22}, a_{13} each with suffixes whose sum is 4; and so on. Given any term in the array, we can assign to it a definite place in the single sequence. We write

$$ b_1 = a_{11}, \qquad b_2 = a_{21}, \qquad b_3 = a_{12}, \qquad b_4 = a_{31}, \ldots $$

and consider $\sum_{n=1}^{\infty} b_n$.

Let
$$ R_m = \sum_{n=1}^{\infty} a_{mn}, \qquad R = \sum_{m=1}^{\infty} R_m, $$
$$ \sigma_N = b_1 + b_2 + \ldots + b_N. $$

Whatever value we give N, we can find a corresponding M such that $R_1 + R_2 + \ldots + R_M$ will contain all the terms of σ_N and others besides. Thus for each N there is a corresponding M such that

$$ \sigma_N < \sum_{m=1}^{M} R_m < R. $$

Hence $\sum b_n$ is a convergent series and, if B is its sum,

$$ B \leqslant R. \tag{1} $$

Second step. Again, if λ is any number less than R, then $\frac{1}{2}(\lambda+R) < R$, which is the sum of $\sum R_n$. Hence there is (by Theorem 3) a suffix k such that

$$R_1+R_2+...+R_k > \tfrac{1}{2}(\lambda+R). \qquad (2)$$

This number k having been fixed, there is (again by Theorem 3) a suffix n such that

$$a_{11}+...+a_{1n} > R_1-\frac{1}{2k}(R-\lambda),$$

$$a_{21}+...+a_{2n} > R_2-\frac{1}{2k}(R-\lambda),$$

$$\cdot \quad \cdot \quad \cdot \quad \cdot \quad \cdot \quad \cdot \quad \cdot \quad \cdot \quad \cdot$$

$$a_{k1}+...+a_{kn} > R_k-\frac{1}{2k}(R-\lambda).$$

But, the numbers k and n having been fixed, there is a number N such that $b_1+b_2+...+b_N$ contains all the terms on the left of these inequalities and others besides. Hence, there is an N for which

$$\sigma_N > R_1+R_2+...+R_k-\tfrac{1}{2}(R-\lambda)$$
$$> \tfrac{1}{2}(R+\lambda)-\tfrac{1}{2}(R-\lambda), \quad \text{by (2)}.$$

It follows that B, which is the upper bound of the sequence (σ_n), exceeds $\tfrac{1}{2}(R+\lambda)-\tfrac{1}{2}(R-\lambda)$, that is, λ. Hence B exceeds any number less than R. Hence

$$B \geqslant R. \qquad (3)$$

From (1) and (3), $\qquad B = R.$

Third step. We now prove that if B is finite, then the sum by columns, C, is finite and equal to B.

Consider $\qquad a_{11}+a_{21}+...+a_{n1}+....$ $\qquad (4)$

The sum of the first n terms, where n is any given number, is less than σ_N if we choose N large enough; also, $\sigma_N < B$. Hence series (4) has a finite sum, C_1 say.

Similarly, each column has a finite sum. Let the sums be $C_1, C_2,...,C_m,...$.

Let M be an arbitrary positive integer. Then, as in the

second step, there is, given any positive δ, a number n such that

$$a_{11}+\ldots+a_{n1} > C_1-\delta\frac{B}{2M}$$

$$a_{12}+\ldots+a_{n2} > C_2-\delta\frac{B}{2M}$$

$$\cdot \quad \cdot \quad \cdot \quad \cdot \quad \cdot \quad \cdot \quad \cdot$$

$$a_{1M}+\ldots+a_{nM} > C_M-\delta\frac{B}{2M}.$$

The sum of all the terms on the left of these inequalities is less than B. Hence
$$B > C_1+C_2+\ldots+C_M-\tfrac{1}{2}\delta B.$$
Hence the infinite series $\sum C_m$ has a sum which is *less* than $B(1+\delta)$ for every positive δ. That is, $C \leqslant B$.

But we can repeat the argument of the first step to show that $B \leqslant C$. Hence $B = C$.

COROLLARY. *If each a_{mn} in the array is positive, and if we know that $\sum b_n$ has a finite sum B, then the array has a sum by rows and a sum by columns, each equal to B.*

By the argument of the third step, we obtain $B = C$; and by the same argument applied to rows we obtain $B = R$.

A convenient name for B is 'the sum by diagonals'.

3. Absolutely convergent double series

THEOREM 58. *If the array*

$$\begin{array}{ccccccc}
a_{11} & a_{12} & \cdot & \cdot & \cdot & a_{1n} & \cdot & \cdot \\
a_{21} & a_{22} & \cdot & \cdot & \cdot & a_{2n} & \cdot & \cdot \\
& \cdot & \cdot & \cdot & \cdot & \cdot & \cdot & \cdot & \cdot \\
a_{m1} & a_{m2} & \cdot & \cdot & \cdot & a_{mn} & \cdot & \cdot \\
& \cdot & \cdot & \cdot & \cdot & \cdot & \cdot & \cdot & \cdot
\end{array}$$

is such that the array got by replacing a_{rs} by its absolute value, $|a_{rs}|$, has a finite sum by rows, then the original array has a finite sum by rows R, a finite sum by columns C, and a finite sum by diagonals B; moreover, $R = C = B$.

Consider two arrays, of which the first consists of the positive terms of the given array, and zeros in the places of all the negative terms. This array will have a finite sum by rows, R' say. By Theorem 57, it has a finite sum by columns, C' say, and a finite sum by diagonals, B' say. Moreover, again by Theorem 57,

$$R' = C' = B'.$$

Let the second array consist of the negative terms of the given array, but with the sign changed, and zeros in the places of all the positive terms. Then, with an obvious notation,

$$R'' = C'' = B''$$

as before.

It is easy to prove that $R = R' - R''$, that $C = C' - C''$, and that $B = B' - B''$.

COROLLARY. *The result of Theorem 58 also holds when the a_{mn} are complex numbers.*

We merely need to write $a_{mn} = \alpha_{mn} + i\beta_{mn}$ and to consider the real and imaginary parts separately.

4. An example

$$\frac{z}{1+z^2} + \frac{z^2}{1+z^4} + \frac{z^3}{1+z^6} + \cdots \tag{1}$$

can be considered as the sum by rows of

$$
\begin{array}{cccccccc}
z & -z^3 & +z^5 & -z^7 & . & . & . \\
z^2 & -z^6 & +z^{10} & -z^{14} & . & . & . \\
z^3 & -z^9 & +z^{15} & -z^{21} & . & . & . \\
. & . & . & . & . & . & . & . \\
\end{array}
$$

The array with absolute values has a finite sum by rows if

$$\frac{|z|}{1-|z|^2} + \frac{|z|^2}{1-|z|^4} + \frac{|z|^3}{1-|z|^6} + \cdots \tag{2}$$

has a finite sum. But, if δ is any positive number less than unity, and if $|z| \leqslant 1-\delta$, then $1-|z| \geqslant \delta$, and so

$$1-|z|^2 > \delta, \qquad 1-|z|^4 > \delta, \qquad \ldots, \qquad 1-|z|^{2n} > \delta.$$

Thus the terms of the series (2) are less than those of

$$\delta^{-1}\{|z| + |z|^2 + |z|^3 + \cdots\}.$$

Hence (2) has a finite sum whenever $|z| < 1$.

The sum by columns of the original array is

$$\frac{z}{1-z} - \frac{z^3}{1-z^3} + \frac{z^5}{1-z^5} - \ldots. \tag{3}$$

Hence (1) and (3) are equal when $|z| < 1$.

EXAMPLES XXII

Some of these examples are taken from Bromwich, *Theory of Infinite Series*.

1. Given that, when $t > 0$,

$$\frac{1}{t^2} = \frac{1}{t(t+1)} + \frac{1}{t(t+1)(t+2)} + \frac{1.2}{t(t+1)(t+2)(t+3)} + \ldots,$$

write down the array whose sum by rows is

$$t^{-2} + (t+1)^{-2} + (t+2)^{-2} + \ldots$$

and hence show that this series is equal to

$$\frac{1}{t} + \frac{1}{2t(t+1)} + \frac{1.2}{3t(t+1)(t+2)} + \ldots.$$

HINT.
$$\frac{1}{t(t+1)(t+2)} = \frac{1}{2}\left\{\frac{1}{t(t+1)} - \frac{1}{(t+1)(t+2)}\right\}$$

2. (*Harder.*) Prove that, when $|x| < 1$,

$$\frac{x}{1-x} + \frac{x^2}{1-x^2} + \frac{x^3}{1-x^3} + \ldots = x\frac{1+x}{1-x} + x^4\frac{1+x^2}{1-x^2} + x^9\frac{1+x^3}{1-x^3} + x^{16}\frac{1+x^4}{1-x^4} + \ldots.$$

[An extension of Theorem 57 is required in that the right-hand side is not a sum by columns.]

3. Prove that, when $|x| < 1$,

$$\frac{x}{1+x^2} + \frac{x^3}{1+x^6} + \frac{x^5}{1+x^{10}} + \ldots = \frac{x}{1-x^2} - \frac{x^3}{1-x^6} + \frac{x^5}{1-x^{10}} - \ldots,$$

$$\frac{x}{1+x^2} - \frac{x^2}{1+x^4} + \frac{x^3}{1+x^6} - \ldots = \frac{x}{1+x} - \frac{x^3}{1+x^3} + \frac{x^5}{1+x^5} - \ldots.$$

4. Show that, if $|x| < 1$,

$$\frac{x}{1+x} - \frac{2x^2}{1+x^2} + \frac{3x^3}{1+x^3} - \ldots = \frac{x}{(1+x)^2} - \frac{x^2}{(1+x^2)^2} + \frac{x^3}{(1+x^3)^2} - \ldots,$$

$$\frac{x}{1-x^2} + \frac{3x^3}{1-x^6} + \frac{5x^5}{1-x^{10}} + \ldots = \frac{x(1+x^2)}{(1-x^2)^2} + \frac{x^3(1+x^6)}{(1-x^6)^2} + \ldots.$$

5. Show that, when $|q| < 1$,

$$1 + \frac{8q}{1-q} + \frac{16q^2}{1+q^2} + \frac{24q^3}{1-q^3} + \ldots = 1 + \frac{8q}{(1-q)^2} + \frac{8q^2}{(1+q^2)^2} + \frac{8q^3}{(1-q^3)^2} + \ldots.$$

6. Prove that, when $0 < c < 1$,

$$c \sum_{n=1}^{\infty} n^{-1-c} - \frac{c(c+1)}{2!} \sum_{n=1}^{\infty} n^{-2-c} + \frac{c(c+1)(c+2)}{3!} \sum_{n=1}^{\infty} n^{-3-c} - \ldots = 1.$$

7. If the terms a_{mn} of a doubly infinite array can be arranged in a single sequence (b_n) such that $\sum |b_n|$ is convergent, prove (*vide* Theorems 57, Corollary, and 58) that the double series has a sum by rows or columns equal to $\sum b_n$.

8. (*Harder.*) In the double series

$$\sum_{m,n}' (m^2 + n^2)^{-\alpha},$$

where both m and n run from $-\infty$ to $+\infty$, and the dash denotes the omission of the term $m = n = 0$, show that the number of terms for which $|m| + |n| = r$, a positive integer, is $4r$; that for each such term $r^2 \geqslant m^2 + n^2 \geqslant \frac{1}{2}r^2$. Hence show that the double series converges if and only if $\sum r^{1-2\alpha}$ does.

CHAPTER XVIII

INFINITE PRODUCTS

1. The convergence of infinite products

1.1. We recall three properties that were proved in Chapter XII. These are:

(i) if $\alpha_n \to \alpha$, then $e^{\alpha_n} \to e^{\alpha}$;

(ii) $\log(1+x) < x$ when x is positive;

(iii) $\xi < \log\dfrac{1}{1-\xi} < \dfrac{\xi}{1-\xi}$ when $0 < \xi < 1$.

1.2. We say that the infinite product

$$\prod_{n=1}^{\infty} u_n$$

is convergent if $p_n \equiv u_1 u_2 \ldots u_n$ tends to a finite limit v as n tends to infinity; v is called the 'value' of the product.

If all the u_n are positive, we may write

$$p_n = e^{\log u_1} e^{\log u_2} \ldots e^{\log u_n}$$
$$= e^{\log u_1 + \log u_2 + \ldots + \log u_n}.$$

By (i) above, if $\sum \log u_n$ is convergent and u is its sum, then

$$p_n \to e^u \quad \text{as } n \to \infty.$$

Moreover, if $\sum \log u_n$ diverges to plus infinity, then $p_n \to +\infty$, and if $\sum \log u_n$ diverges to minus infinity, then $p_n \to 0$.

1.3. THEOREM 59. *Let (a_n) be a sequence of positive numbers less than unity. Then, as $m \to \infty$,*

$$\prod_{n=1}^{m} (1+a_n), \qquad \prod_{n=1}^{m} (1-a_n)$$

converge to finite, non-zero, limits if $\sum a_n$ is convergent; if $\sum a_n$ is divergent, then the first product $\to +\infty$, and the second product $\to 0$.

We note first that, by the hypothesis $0 < a_n < 1$,

$$\log(1+a_n), \qquad \{-\log(1-a_n)\}$$

are positive numbers.

Let $\sum a_n$ be convergent. Then, by (ii) of § 1.1,

$$\log(1+a_n) < a_n$$

and $\sum \log(1+a_n)$ is therefore convergent. Hence, by (i) of § 1.1, the first product converges to a finite, non-zero, limit.

Again, by (iii) of § 1.1,

$$\{-\log(1-a_n)\} < \frac{a_n}{1-a_n} < Ka_n,$$

because $(1-a_n)^{-1}$ is a sequence that $\to 1$.

$$[a_n \to 0 \quad \text{since } \sum a_n \text{ is convergent.}]$$

Hence $\sum \{-\log(1-a_n)\}$ is convergent; so also is $\sum \log(1-a_n)$, and the second product converges to a finite, non-zero, limit.

Now let $\sum a_n$ be divergent. Then, without recourse to logarithms,

$$(1+a_1)(1+a_2) = 1+a_1+a_2+a_1a_2 > 1+a_1+a_2,$$

and $\quad (1+a_1)(1+a_2)...(1+a_n) > 1+a_1+a_2+...+a_n.$

Hence the product

$$(1+a_1)(1+a_2)...(1+a_n)$$

increases indefinitely.

Further, $\qquad 1-a_n < \dfrac{1}{1+a_n},$

as we see by cross-multiplication. Hence

$$(1-a_1)(1-a_2)...(1-a_n)$$

is less than the reciprocal of $(1+a_1)...(1+a_n)$, and so tends to zero.

1.4. As in the case of series, $a_n \to 0$ is a necessary but by no means sufficient condition that $\prod (1+a_n)$ should converge. For, if the product has a finite, non-zero, value, P say, then

$$(1+a_1)...(1+a_{n-1}) \quad \text{and} \quad (1+a_1)...(1+a_n)$$

each converges to P as $n \to \infty$. Hence $1+a_n \to 1$.

2. Absolute convergence

2.1. The series $\sum \log(1+a_n)$ will have a sum independent of the order of its terms, and so $\prod (1+a_n)$ will have a value independent of the order of its terms, if $\sum |\log(1+a_n)|$ is convergent.

Before we give a formal definition of the absolute convergence of a product we prove that

A necessary and sufficient condition for $\sum |\log(1+a_n)|$ to be convergent is that $\sum |a_n|$ be convergent.

If the first series is convergent, then so is $\sum \log(1+a_n)$, so that $\log(1+a_n) \to 0$, and $1+a_n \to 1$. Hence $a_n \to 0$ and

$$\exists\ N\ .\ |a_n| < \tfrac{1}{2}\quad\text{when } n \geqslant N.$$

When $n \geqslant N$ we have

$$\log(1+a_n) = a_n - \tfrac{1}{2}a_n^2 + \tfrac{1}{3}a_n^3 - \dots,$$

and so

$$\left| \frac{\log(1+a_n)}{a_n} - 1 \right| \leqslant \left| -\frac{a_n}{2} + \frac{a_n^2}{3} - \dots \right|$$

$$\leqslant \frac{1}{2^2} + \frac{1}{2^3} + \dots = \frac{1}{2}.$$

Hence

$$\frac{1}{2} \leqslant \left| \frac{\log(1+a_n)}{a_n} \right| \leqslant \frac{3}{2}. \tag{1}$$

Accordingly, $|a_n| \leqslant 2|\log(1+a_n)|$ when $n \geqslant N$, and so $\sum |a_n|$ is convergent.

If $\sum |a_n|$ is convergent, then again $a_n \to 0$, and (1) proves that $|\log(1+a_n)| \leqslant \tfrac{3}{2}|a_n|$ when $n \geqslant N$. Hence $\sum |\log(1+a_n)|$ is convergent.

2.2. DEFINITION. *The product $\prod (1+a_n)$ is said to be absolutely convergent if $\sum a_n$ is absolutely convergent.*

By what we have proved in § 2.1, this definition is equivalent to saying that the product is absolutely convergent when $\sum \log(1+a_n)$ is absolutely convergent. Sometimes the one and sometimes the other definition will be found in more advanced work.

3. Uniform convergence

If the a_n are functions of a variable x, and

$$p_n(x) = \{1+a_1(x)\}\dots\{1+a_n(x)\},$$

the product is said to be uniformly convergent if the sequence $p_n(x)$ is. The properties of uniformly convergent sequences have been considered in Chapter XI.

The one test that is adapted to products is the analogue of the M test for series.

THEOREM 60. *If $|a_n(x)| \leqslant M_n$ when $a \leqslant x \leqslant b$, and if $\sum M_n$ is a convergent series of positive constants, then the sequence $p_n(x)$ converges uniformly in $a \leqslant x \leqslant b$.*

By the M test (Theorem 35), $\sum |a_n(x)|$ is uniformly convergent in (a, b). Hence, by an adaptation of § 2.1, $\sum |\log\{1+a_n(x)\}|$, and so also $\sum \log\{1+a_n(x)\}$, converges uniformly in (a, b). If the latter series converges uniformly to the sum $u(x)$, it follows that $p_n(x)$ converges uniformly to $e^{u(x)}$.

4. A test for non-absolute convergence

THEOREM 61. *If* $-1 < a_n < 1$, *and if* $\sum a_n^2$ *is convergent, then*

(i) $\prod (1+a_n)$ *converges when* $\sum a_n$ *converges,*

(ii) $\prod (1+a_n) \to +\infty$ *when* $\sum a_n \to +\infty$,

(iii) $\prod (1+a_n) \to 0$ *when* $\sum a_n \to -\infty$.

If $-1 < a_n < 1$, *and if* $\sum a_n^2$ *is divergent, then* $\prod (1+a_n) \to 0$ *when* $\sum a_n$ *is bounded.*

The proof depends upon the identity

$$\frac{t}{1+t} = 1 - \frac{1}{1+t},$$

which, upon integration, gives

$$\int_0^y \frac{t \, dt}{1+t} = y - \log(1+y) \tag{1}$$

when $-1 < y < 1$. Moreover, the left-hand side of (1) is clearly positive when y is positive; when y is negative, equal to $-z$ say, the substitution $t = -\theta$ gives

$$\int_0^y \frac{t \, dt}{1+t} = \int_0^z \frac{\theta \, d\theta}{1-\theta} > 0,$$

and again the left-hand side of (1) is positive.

Hence, for any integers N and p,

$$0 < \sum_{r=N}^{N+p} a_r - \sum_{r=N}^{N+p} \log(1+a_r) = \sum_{r=N}^{N+p} \int_0^{a_r} \frac{t \, dt}{1+t}. \tag{2}$$

Suppose now that $\sum a_n^2$ is convergent. Then $a_n \to 0$, $1+a_n \to 1$ and, since $1+a_n > 0$ for each n, there is a positive K such that (Chap. V, § 1.2, lemma)

$$1+a_n \geqslant K > 0 \quad \text{for all } n.$$

Moreover, since some a_n are negative, $K < 1$.

It follows that

$$\text{when } a_r > 0, \quad \int_0^{a_r} \frac{t\,dt}{1+t} < \int_0^{a_r} t\,dt = \tfrac{1}{2}a_r^2 < \frac{1}{2K}a_r^2;$$

$$\text{when } a_r < 0, \quad \int_0^{a_r} \frac{t\,dt}{1+t} = \int_0^{|a_r|} \frac{\theta\,d\theta}{1-\theta} < \frac{1}{K}\int_0^{|a_r|} \theta\,d\theta = \frac{1}{2K}a_r^2.$$

Hence, from (2),

$$0 < \sum_{r=N}^{N+p} a_r - \sum_{r=N}^{N+p} \log(1+a_r) \leqslant \frac{1}{2K}\sum_{r=N}^{N+p} a_r^2. \tag{3}$$

Hence, by the general convergence principle (Theorem 21), if both $\sum a_n$ and $\sum a_n^2$ are convergent, then $\sum \log(1+a_n)$ is also convergent, and (i) is proved.

If $\sum a_n^2$ is convergent, and if $\sum a_n \to +\infty$, then (3) shows that $\sum \log(1+a_r)$ must also $\to +\infty$, and (ii) is proved.

If $\sum a_n^2$ is convergent, and if $\sum a_n \to -\infty$, then (3) shows that $\sum \log(1+a_r)$ must $\to -\infty$, and (iii) is proved.

The last part of the theorem follows from (2) on observing that, in each integral, $0 < 1+t < 2$ throughout the range of integration, so that

$$\sum_{r=N}^{N+p} a_r - \sum_{r=N}^{N+p} \log(1+a_r) > \tfrac{1}{2}\sum_{r=N}^{N+p} \int_0^{|a_r|} t\,dt = \tfrac{1}{4}\sum_{r=N}^{N+p} a_r^2.$$

EXAMPLES XXIII

1. Prove that each of the products

$$\prod_{n=1}^{\infty}\left(1+\frac{1}{n^2}\right), \qquad \prod_{n=2}^{\infty}\left(1-\frac{1}{n^2}\right), \qquad \prod_{n=1}^{\infty}\left(1+\sin^2\frac{\theta}{n}\right)$$

converges to a finite, non-zero, limit.

2. Prove that

$$\prod_{n=2}^{N}\left(1-\frac{1}{n}\right), \qquad \prod_{n=1}^{N}\left(1-\frac{x}{n}\right) \quad (x > 0)$$

each tends to zero as $N \to \infty$.

3. Prove that the second product in Example 2 tends to infinity when $x < 0$.

4. Prove that

$$\left|\log\left(1+\frac{x}{n}\right)-\frac{x}{n}\right| = \left|-\frac{x^2}{2n^2}+\frac{x^3}{3n^3}-...\right| < \frac{|x^2|}{n^2}\left\{1+\frac{|x|}{n}+\frac{|x|^2}{n^2}+...\right\}.$$

Hence show that, if $|x| < A$,

$$\left|\log\left(1+\frac{x}{n}\right)-\frac{x}{n}\right| < \frac{A^2}{n^2}\left\{1+\frac{1}{2}+\frac{1}{2^2}+...\right\}$$

when $n > 2A$.

5. Prove that
$$\prod_{n=1}^{\infty}\left(1+\frac{x}{n}\right)e^{-x/n}$$

is (i) absolutely convergent for any fixed x,
(ii) uniformly convergent for $|x| \leqslant A$, where A is any fixed number.

6. Prove that
$$\prod_{n=1}^{\infty}\left(1-\frac{x^2}{n^2\pi^2}\right)$$

is (i) absolutely convergent for any fixed x,
(ii) uniformly convergent for $|x| \leqslant A$, where A is any fixed number.

7. Verify the identity

$$\left(1-\frac{x}{1}\right)\left(1-\frac{x}{2}\right)...\left(1-\frac{x}{n}\right) = 1-x+\frac{x(x-1)}{2!}-...+(-)^n\frac{x(x-1)...(x-n+1)}{n!}.$$

Prove that, when $x > 0$, the product $\to 0$ as $n \to \infty$.

8. By means of Example 7 show that

$$1-x+\frac{x(x-1)}{2!}-... = 0$$

when $x > 0$.

9. Prove that, when $|q| < 1$, each of the products

$$q_0 = \prod(1-q^{2n}), \qquad q_1 = \prod(1+q^{2n}),$$
$$q_2 = \prod(1+q^{2n-1}), \qquad q_3 = \prod(1-q^{2n-1}), \qquad (n = 1, 2, ...)$$

is absolutely convergent.
Prove also that

$$q_0 q_3 = \prod(1-q^n), \qquad q_1 q_2 = \prod(1+q^n),$$

and
$$q_1 q_2 q_3 = 1;$$

further that

$$(1+q)(1+q^2)(1+q^3)... = 1/(1-q)(1-q^3)(1-q^5)....$$

10. Prove that, when $|x| < 1$,

$$(1+x)(1+x^2)(1+x^4)(1+x^8)... = (1-x)^{-1}.$$

11. Evaluate $\quad 2^n \sin \dfrac{x}{2^n} . \cos \dfrac{x}{2^n} \cos \dfrac{x}{2^{n-1}} \dots \cos \dfrac{x}{2},$

and hence prove that

$$\cos \frac{x}{2} \cos \frac{x}{2^2} \cos \frac{x}{2^3} \dots = \frac{\sin x}{x}.$$

12. (*Harder.*) Find the limit as $n \to \infty$ of

$$\prod_{m=0}^{n} \{(1-q^{2^m})/(1+q^{2^m})\}^{(\frac{1}{2})^m}$$

when $0 < q < 1$.

13. Prove that

$$\frac{1}{t} - \frac{1}{t+1} = \frac{1}{t(t+1)},$$

$$\frac{1}{t} - \frac{1}{t+1} - \frac{1}{(t+1)(t+2)} = \frac{2}{t(t+1)(t+2)},$$

and, more generally, that

$$\frac{1}{t} - \frac{1}{t+1} - \sum_{r=1}^{n-1} \frac{r!}{(t+1)\dots(t+r+1)} = \frac{n!}{t(t+1)\dots(t+n)}.$$

14. Use Examples 3 and 13 to prove that

$$\frac{1}{t} = \frac{1}{t+1} + \sum_{n=1}^{\infty} \frac{n!}{(t+1)(t+2)\dots(t+n+1)}.$$

15. Prove that if $b > a$, then

$$\frac{a(a+1)\dots(a+n)}{b(b+1)\dots(b+n)} \to 0$$

provided that b is neither zero nor a negative integer.

HINT. $\qquad \dfrac{b+n}{a+n} = 1 + \dfrac{b-a}{a+n},$

and the series $\sum (a+n)^{-1}$ is a divergent series whose terms are ultimately positive.

CHAPTER XIX

THEOREMS ON LIMITS: CESÀRO SUMS

1. A general theorem on limits

1.1. THEOREM 62. *If (b_n) is a sequence of positive numbers that increase steadily to $+\infty$, and if the sequence (a_n) is such that*

$$\frac{a_{n+1}-a_n}{b_{n+1}-b_n} \to a \text{ finite limit } l, \tag{1}$$

then also
$$\frac{a_n}{b_n} \to l. \tag{2}$$

In the first instance, suppose that $l = 0$. Then, by hypothesis,

$$\epsilon, k > 0; \quad \exists \, N \; . \; -\epsilon k < \frac{a_{n+1}-a_n}{b_{n+1}-b_n} < \epsilon k \quad \text{when } n \geqslant N.$$

Since $b_{n+1}-b_n$ is positive, we have

$$-\epsilon k(b_{n+1}-b_n) < a_{n+1}-a_n < \epsilon k(b_{n+1}-b_n).$$

Write down this inequality for $n = N, N+1, ..., N+p-1$, and add: we obtain

$$-\epsilon k(b_{N+p}-b_N) < a_{N+p}-a_N < \epsilon k(b_{N+p}-b_N).$$

A fortiori
$$-\epsilon k b_{N+p} < a_{N+p}-a_N < \epsilon k b_{N+p}.$$

Hence
$$\left|\frac{a_{N+p}}{b_{N+p}}\right| \leqslant \left|\frac{a_{N+p}-a_N}{b_{N+p}}\right| + \left|\frac{a_N}{b_{N+p}}\right|$$
$$< \epsilon k + \frac{|a_N|}{b_{N+p}}.$$

But, if N is kept fixed and $p \to \infty$, $b_{N+p} \to \infty$ (by hypothesis). Hence $\exists \, P \; . \; |a_N|/b_{N+p} < \epsilon k$ when $p \geqslant P$. If, then, we take $k = \frac{1}{2}$ at the start, we have proved that

$$\epsilon > 0; \quad \exists \text{ numbers } N, P \; . \; \left|\frac{a_n}{b_n}\right| < \epsilon \quad \text{when } n \geqslant N+P,$$

and the theorem, with $l = 0$, is proved.

Now suppose that $l \neq 0$ in (1). Write

$$A_n = a_n - lb_n,$$

so that
$$\frac{A_{n+1}-A_n}{b_{n+1}-b_n} = \frac{a_{n+1}-a_n}{b_{n+1}-b_n} - l \to 0.$$

Then, by what we have already proved,

$$\frac{A_n}{b_n} \to 0, \quad \text{i.e.} \quad \frac{a_n}{b_n} - l \to 0,$$

and the theorem is proved when l has any value.

1.2. The converse of the theorem is not true as a general proposition. Because (2) holds it does not follow that

$$(a_{n+1} - a_n)/(b_{n+1} - b_n)$$

will tend to a limit. For example, if

$$a_{2n} = 0, \qquad a_{2n+1} = 1, \qquad b_n = n,$$

then $(a_n/b_n) \to 0$; but

$$\frac{a_{2n+1} - a_{2n}}{b_{2n+1} - b_{2n}} = 1, \qquad \frac{a_{2n} - a_{2n-1}}{b_{2n} - b_{2n-1}} = -1,$$

so that $(a_{n+1} - a_n)/(b_{n+1} - b_n)$ cannot tend to a limit.

2. Particular cases of Theorem 62

2.1. When $b_n = n$, the theorem takes the form

(i) if $a_{n+1} - a_n \to l$, then also $\dfrac{a_n}{n} \to l$.

When we put $a_n = \alpha_1 + \alpha_2 + \ldots + \alpha_n$ in (i), we have

(ii) if $\alpha_{n+1} \to l$, then also $\dfrac{\alpha_1 + \alpha_2 + \ldots + \alpha_n}{n} \to l$,

a theorem that is frequently used in advanced work on series.

Turning now to products, we have, on putting

$$\alpha_n = \log \beta_n \quad (\beta_n > 0),$$

(iii) if $\beta_n \to \beta$, then also $\sqrt[n]{(\beta_1 \beta_2 \ldots \beta_n)} \to \beta$.

Again, if we put

$$\beta_1 = |u_1|, \qquad \beta_n = |u_n/u_{n-1}| \quad (n > 1),$$

we have

(iv) if $|u_n/u_{n-1}| \to \rho$, then also $\sqrt[n]{u_n} \to \rho$.

Finally, as a numerical example, put

$$\beta_n = \left(1 + \frac{1}{n}\right)^n,$$

so that $\beta_n \to e$. Since

$$\beta_1 \beta_2 \ldots \beta_n = \frac{(n+1)^n}{n!},$$

the form (iii) shows that

$$\frac{n+1}{\sqrt[n]{(n!)}} \to e, \quad \text{or} \quad \frac{n}{\sqrt[n]{(n!)}} \to e.$$

2.2. In each of the particular cases (i)–(iv) the remark made in § 1.2 about the general theorem still holds. The first limit need not exist because the second does.

3. Conventional sums of non-convergent series

3.1. Suppose a sequence (s_n) is given. Then the sequence of its arithmetic means

$$t_n = \frac{s_1 + s_2 + \dots + s_n}{n} \quad (n = 1, 2, 3, \dots)$$

cannot fluctuate with greater violence than does the sequence (s_n); it may well fluctuate with less violence. Modern mathematics makes considerable use of non-convergent series by means of a technique that began with this simple consideration.

The 'sum' of a series, as we have hitherto used the word, is defined thus:

The sum of $\sum u_n$ is s if $s_n = u_1 + u_2 + \dots + u_n$ and $s_n \to s$. There are many series met with in analysis for which (s_n) is not a convergent sequence, although its fluctuations are mild enough to be 'ironed out' by the process of taking arithmetic means; that is to say, (s_n) is not a convergent sequence, but (t_n) is. It is natural to take the limit of t_n as the 'sum', in a special sense, of the series in question. Such a sum is called the $(C, 1)$ sum of the series, the C recalling its inventor Cesàro and the 1 denoting the first of such sums (the second, third,... being derived from similar, but less simple, considerations).

DEFINITION. *The series $\sum u_n$ is said to have a $(C, 1)$ sum s if $t_n \to s$ as $n \to \infty$, where*

$$t_n \equiv \frac{s_1 + s_2 + \dots + s_n}{n}, \qquad s_n \equiv u_1 + u_2 + \dots + u_n.$$

3.2. It would lead to intolerable complications if it so happened that a series might have one sum in the ordinary (convergent series) sense and another sum in the $(C, 1)$ sense. But, as we see by Theorem 62, particular case (ii),

$$\text{if } s_n \to s, \quad \text{then } t_n \to s;$$

that is to say, if a series is convergent, then its $(C, 1)$ sum is the same as its sum in the ordinary sense.

As it is rather unsatisfactory to have such an indirect proof as the one we have just given, we shall give a direct proof.

THEOREM 63. *If $s_n \to s$, and if*

$$t_n = \frac{s_1 + s_2 + \ldots + s_n}{n},$$

then $t_n \to s$.

We have at once

$$t_n - s = \frac{1}{n}\{(s_1 - s) + (s_2 - s) + \ldots + (s_n - s)\}.$$

The sequence $s_n - s \to 0$, and so, by Theorem 1, is bounded. Hence

(i) $\exists \ K \ . \ |s_n - s| < K$ for all n,

(ii) $\epsilon > 0; \ \exists \ N \ . \ |s_n - s| < \tfrac{1}{2}\epsilon$ when $n \geqslant N$.

Take a definite such value of $N \ (> 1)$ and let $n > N$. Then

$$|t_n - s| < \frac{(N-1)K}{n} + \frac{(n-N+1)\epsilon}{2n}$$

$$< \frac{(N-1)K}{n} + \tfrac{1}{2}\epsilon.$$

But N, K are fixed, and we can make the last expression less than ϵ by taking $n \geqslant 2(N-1)K\epsilon^{-1}$. Hence

$$\epsilon > 0; \ \exists \ N_1 \ . \ |t_n - s| < \epsilon \quad \text{when } n \geqslant N_1.$$

4. The more general form of Theorem 62

The full force of Theorem 62 cannot be realized from the elementary point of view, which confines itself to sequences (α_n) that tend to a limit. The two limits

$$\overline{\lim} \, \alpha_n \quad \text{and} \quad \underline{\lim} \, \alpha_n$$

are necessary to a full statement of Theorem 62.

We refer the reader to the appendix for a definition of these;

meanwhile, we note that, if (b_n) is a sequence of positive numbers that increase steadily to $+\infty$, then

$$\overline{\lim}\frac{a_{n+1}-a_n}{b_{n+1}-b_n} \geqslant \overline{\lim}\frac{a_n}{b_n} \geqslant \underline{\lim}\frac{a_n}{b_n} \geqslant \underline{\lim}\frac{a_{n+1}-a_n}{b_{n+1}-b_n}; \qquad (1)$$

and a sequence (α_n) converges to a finite limit α if, and only if,

$$\overline{\lim}\,\alpha_n = \underline{\lim}\,\alpha_n = \alpha.$$

If the two extremes of (1) are equal, the middle terms must be equal and have the same value as the extremes; but the converse is not necessarily true, since the middle terms may be equal and the extremes unequal.

Examples XXIV

1. Prove that, if

$$S_n^{(r)} = s_n + rs_{n-1} + \frac{r(r+1)}{2!}s_{n-2} + \dots + \frac{r(r+1)\dots(r+n-1)}{n!}s_0,$$

and

$$A_n^{(r)} = (r+1)(r+2)\dots(r+n)/n!,$$

and if $S_n^{(r-1)}/A_n^{(r-1)} \to l$, then, provided that $r > 0$,

$$S_n^{(r)}/A_n^{(r)} \to l.$$

$$\left[S_{n+1}^{(r)} - S_n^{(r)} = S_{n+1}^{(r-1)}; \quad A_{n+1}^{(r)} - A_n^{(r)} = A_{n+1}^{(r-1)}.\right]$$

2. If $s_n \to s$ as $n \to \infty$, prove that each of the sequences

(i) $2n^{-2}(s_n + 2s_{n-1} + \dots + ns_1)$,

(ii) $\dfrac{1}{n}\left\{s_1\left(1+\dfrac{1}{2}+\dots+\dfrac{1}{n}\right) + s_2\left(\dfrac{1}{2}+\dfrac{1}{3}+\dots+\dfrac{1}{n}\right) + \dots + s_n\left(\dfrac{1}{n}\right)\right\}$

also tends to s.

3. (*Harder.*) $P(n)$ denotes the sum of the products, in pairs, of the pth powers of the first n positive integers; prove that, if $p+1 > 0$,

$$\frac{P(n)}{(n+1)^{2p+2}} \to \frac{1}{2(p+1)^2} \quad \text{as } n \to \infty.$$

4. Prove that the $(C, 1)$ sum of the series

$$1 - 1 + 1 - 1 + 1 - \dots$$

is $\tfrac{1}{2}$.

5. If $a_n \to a$ and $b_n \to b$, then

$$\frac{1}{n}(a_1 b_n + a_2 b_{n-1} + \dots + a_n b_1) \to ab.$$

Hint. Prove the theorem first when $a = b = 0$. To do this, note that *one* of the suffixes $r, n-r$ must exceed N if $n > 2N$. Let $|a_n| < A$, $|b_n| < B$ for all n. We have

$$\epsilon, k > 0; \quad \exists \ N \ . \ |a_n| < \epsilon k, \quad |b_n| < \epsilon k \quad \text{when } n \geqslant N.$$

Hence, when $n > 2N$ and K is any fixed number $\geqslant A, B$,

$$\frac{1}{n}(a_1 b_n + \ldots + a_n b_1) < K\epsilon k,$$

and the result follows on taking $k = 1/K$.

6. If $\sum c_n$ is a divergent series of positive terms and $(d_n/c_n) \rightarrow s$, then also $\{(d_1 + d_2 + \ldots + d_n)/(c_1 + c_2 + \ldots + c_n)\} \rightarrow s$.

HINT. Put $c_1 + c_2 + \ldots + c_n = b_n$ in Theorem 62.

7. If p_n is positive and $\{p_n/(p_0 + \ldots + p_n)\} \rightarrow 0$, prove that $s_n \rightarrow s$ implies

$$\frac{p_n s_0 + p_{n-1} s_1 + \ldots + p_0 s_n}{p_n + p_{n-1} + \ldots + p_0} \rightarrow s.$$

HINT. Cf. the method of proving Theorem 63.

CHAPTER XX

FOURIER SERIES

1. Periodic functions

A function $f(x)$ such that $f(x) = f(x+\Omega)$ for all values of x, where Ω is a constant, is called a periodic function of x, and Ω is called the period of the function. For example, $\sin x$ and $\cos x$ are periodic functions.

If we are given a series

$$\tfrac{1}{2}a_0 + \sum_{n=1}^{\infty} (a_n \cos nx + b_n \sin nx) \tag{1}$$

that converges for all values of x, then its sum is necessarily a periodic function of x, for each term is unaltered when $x+2\pi$ replaces x.

The problem of this chapter is to find when, given a periodic function $f(x)$, of period 2π, the function can be expressed as the sum of a series of type (1).

2. Elementary properties

The following facts in integral calculus form the basis of all the subsequent work. Throughout we use m, n to denote positive integers or zero.

$$\int_{-\pi}^{\pi} \cos mx \cos nx \, dx = \tfrac{1}{2} \int_{-\pi}^{\pi} \{\cos(m+n)x + \cos(m-n)x\} \, dx$$

$$= 0, \pi \quad \text{according as } m \neq n, \, m = n;$$

$$\int_{-\pi}^{\pi} \sin mx \sin nx \, dx = \tfrac{1}{2} \int_{-\pi}^{\pi} \{\cos(m-n)x - \cos(m+n)x\} \, dx$$

$$= 0, \pi \quad \text{according as } m \neq n, \, m = n;$$

$$\int_{-\pi}^{\pi} \cos mx \sin nx \, dx = \tfrac{1}{2} \int_{-\pi}^{\pi} \{\sin(n+m)x + \sin(n-m)x\} \, dx$$

$$= 0;$$

$$\int\limits_{-\pi}^{\pi} \cos mx\, dx = 0, 2\pi \quad \text{according as } m > 0, m = 0;$$

$$\int\limits_{-\pi}^{\pi} \sin mx\, dx = 0.$$

3. Fourier series

3.1. If numbers $a_0,\ a_1,\dots,\ a_n,\dots;\ b_1,\ b_2,\dots,\ b_n,\dots$ are derived from a function $f(x)$ by means of the equations

$$\pi a_n = \int\limits_{-\pi}^{\pi} f(t)\cos nt\, dt, \qquad \pi b_n = \int\limits_{-\pi}^{\pi} f(t)\sin nt\, dt, \tag{2}$$

then the series

$$\tfrac{1}{2}a_0 + \sum_{n=1}^{\infty} (a_n \cos nx + b_n \sin nx) \tag{3}$$

is called the *Fourier series* of $f(x)$.

The series (3) is not necessarily convergent because the numbers a_n, b_n are so defined; even if the series is convergent its sum is not necessarily $f(x)$, though it often will be.

The numbers a_n, b_n are called the *Fourier coefficients* of $f(x)$.

3.2. The relations between a function $f(x)$, its Fourier coefficients, and its Fourier series have been the subject of extensive research.†

We shall here prove only two theorems, Theorems 64 and 65, both concerned with stating conditions under which a Fourier series can be used to represent the function from which it is derived.

THEOREM 64. *If the series*

$$\tfrac{1}{2}a_0 + \sum_{n=1}^{\infty} (a_n \cos nx + b_n \sin nx),$$

where the a_n, b_n are constants, is uniformly convergent in $(-\pi, \pi)$, and if $f(x)$ is its sum, then it is the Fourier series of $f(x)$.

† See, for example, A. Zygmund, *Trigonometrical Series* (Math. Monographs, Warsaw, 1935), where the theory of Fourier series is developed.

The proof of this theorem is a straightforward deduction from the properties we have given in § 2. We have

$$f(x) = \tfrac{1}{2}a_0 + \sum_{n=1}^{\infty} (a_n \cos nx + b_n \sin nx). \tag{4}$$

Since the series is uniformly convergent in $(-\pi, \pi)$, we may multiply by $\cos mx$ $(m \geqslant 1)$ and integrate term by term. When the integration is from $-\pi$ to π, all the terms of the resulting series are zero (by § 2) excepting only

$$a_m \int_{-\pi}^{\pi} \cos^2 mx \, dx,$$

whose value is πa_m. Hence

$$\pi a_m = \int_{-\pi}^{\pi} f(x)\cos mx \, dx \quad (m = 1, 2, \dots).$$

Similarly,

$$\pi b_m = \int_{-\pi}^{\pi} f(x)\sin mx \, dx \quad (m = 1, 2, \dots).$$

Finally, on integrating (4) as it stands, the results of § 2 give

$$\int_{-\pi}^{\pi} f(x) \, dx = \tfrac{1}{2}a_0 \int_{-\pi}^{\pi} dx = \pi a_0.$$

This last step shows that the term $\tfrac{1}{2}a_0$ (and not a_0) is necessary if the definition of a_n by means of (2) is to hold for $n = 0$ as well as for $n \geqslant 1$.

3.3. The other theorem we shall prove is much more difficult to establish. It will form the basis of the examples we shall give and is, *par excellence*, the practical form of Fourier's expansion of a function in a series of sines and cosines.

We need a preliminary definition.

DEFINITION. *If $f(x+h)$ tends to a definite limit as h tends to zero through positive values, then this limit is denoted by $f(x+0)$.*

If $f(x-h)$ tends to a definite limit as h tends to zero through positive values, then this limit is denoted by $f(x-0)$.

If a function is continuous at x, then

$$f(x+0) = f(x-0) = f(x).$$

EXAMPLES.

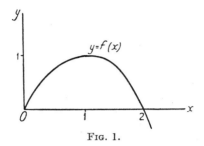

FIG. 1.

In Fig. 1 we have the graph of a continuous function. If we take any definite x, say $x = 1$, then

$$f(1+h) \to f(1) \text{ as } h \to 0, \quad \text{so that } f(1+0) = f(1);$$
$$f(1-h) \to f(1) \text{ as } h \to 0, \quad \text{so that } f(1-0) = f(1).$$

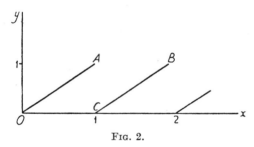

FIG. 2.

In Fig. 2 we have the graph of a function that is discontinuous at $x = 1, 2,\ldots$. When h is small and positive the point $\{1-h, f(1-h)\}$ lies in OA; as $h \to 0$, $f(1-h) \to 1$. That is,

$$f(1-0) = 1.$$

On the other hand, the point $\{1+h, f(1+h)\}$ lies in CB; as $h \to 0$, $f(1+h) \to 0$. That is,

$$f(1+0) = 0.$$

3.4. THEOREM 65. *Let $f(x)$ be a periodic function of period 2π, so that $f(x+2\pi) = f(x)$; let $|f(x)|$ be integrable in $(-\pi, \pi)$ and let a_n, b_n be its Fourier coefficients. Then*

$$\tfrac{1}{2}a_0 + \sum_{n=1}^{\infty} (a_n \cos nx + b_n \sin nx) = \tfrac{1}{2}\{f(x+0)+f(x-0)\} \quad (5)$$

whenever

(i) *the series is convergent*

and (ii) *the limits on the right of* (5) *exist.*

The limits $f(x+0)$ will not exist for all functions: for example,

$$\sin\left(\pi+\frac{1}{h}\right) = -\sin\frac{1}{h}$$

does not approach a definite limit as $h \to 0$.

3.5. We return to a proof of Theorem 65 later. We first dispose of more elementary considerations, assuming meanwhile the main result of Theorem 65, namely, that with the given conditions

'*equation* (5) *holds whenever both sides make sense*'.

Let a function $f(x)$ be given, not necessarily periodic. Define a new function thus:

When $-\pi \leqslant x < \pi$, define $F(x)$ to be $f(x)$; for other values of x let $F(x)$ be defined by the relation

$$F(x+2\pi) = F(x).$$

Then, if $|F(x)|$ is integrable in $(-\pi, \pi)$, its Fourier series, when convergent, has for its sum

$$\tfrac{1}{2}\{F(x+0)+F(x-0)\}.$$

We assume, of course, that these last limits do exist.

In the interval $-\pi < x < \pi$, this is $\tfrac{1}{2}\{f(x+0)+f(x-0)\}$. But

$$F(\pi+h) = F(\pi+h-2\pi) = F(-\pi+h) = f(-\pi+h),$$

and $\qquad\qquad\qquad F(\pi-h) = f(\pi-h),$

so that $\qquad F(\pi+0)+F(\pi-0) = f(-\pi+0)+f(\pi-0).$

Hence the sum of the Fourier series of $F(x)$ at $x = \pi$ is

$$\tfrac{1}{2}\{f(-\pi+0)+f(\pi-0)\}.$$

Outside the interval $(-\pi, \pi)$ the Fourier series is related to $F(x)$ and not to $f(x)$.

3.6. *A worked example. Find the Fourier series that represents e^x in $-\pi < x < \pi$.*

The function e^x is not periodic and so, in order to have an appropriate periodic function, we define a function thus:

Let $\qquad\qquad f(x) \equiv e^x \quad$ when $-\pi \leqslant x < \pi,$

and let $f(x)$ be defined for all other values of x by means of the equation
$$f(x+2\pi) = f(x).$$
For example, the value of $f(x)$ when $x = \frac{3}{2}\pi$ would be given by $f(\frac{3}{2}\pi - 2\pi)$, i.e. $e^{-\frac{1}{2}\pi}$.

The Fourier coefficients of $f(x)$ are given by

$$\pi a_0 = \int_{-\pi}^{\pi} e^x \, dx = 2\sinh\pi,$$

$$\pi a_m = \int_{-\pi}^{\pi} e^x \cos mx \, dx = \frac{(-1)^m}{m^2+1} 2\sinh\pi,$$

$$\pi b_m = \int_{-\pi}^{\pi} e^x \sin mx \, dx = -\frac{(-1)^m m}{m^2+1} 2\sinh\pi.$$

Hence the Fourier series of $f(x)$ is

$$\frac{2\sinh\pi}{\pi} \left\{ \frac{1}{2} + \sum_{n=1}^{\infty} \frac{(-1)^n}{n^2+1} (\cos nx - n\sin nx) \right\} \qquad (6)$$

Each of the series

$$\sum (-1)^n \cos nx/(n^2+1), \qquad \sum (-1)^n n \sin nx/(n^2+1)$$

is convergent [cf. Chap. IX, § 3.5: $(-1)^n \sin nx = \sin n(x+\pi)$].

Moreover, when $-\pi < x < \pi$,

$$f(x+0) = \lim_{h\to 0} e^{x+h} = e^x,$$

$$f(x-0) = \lim_{h\to 0} e^{x-h} = e^x.$$

Hence (6) is equal to e^x when $-\pi < x < \pi$.

When $x = \pi$ or $-\pi$ we must consider carefully how $f(x)$ is defined. By definition, when $h > 0$,

$$f(\pi+h) = f(\pi+h-2\pi) = e^{-\pi+h}, \quad \text{so that } f(\pi+0) = e^{-\pi},$$

$$f(\pi-h) = e^{\pi-h}, \quad \text{so that } f(\pi-0) = e^{\pi}.$$

Hence, when $x = \pi$, the sum of the series (6) is not e^{π}, but is $\frac{1}{2}(e^{-\pi}+e^{\pi})$.

Similarly,

$$f(-\pi+h) = e^{-\pi+h} \quad \text{and} \quad f(-\pi+0) = e^{-\pi},$$

$$f(-\pi-h) = f(-\pi-h+2\pi) = e^{\pi-h} \quad \text{and} \quad f(-\pi-0) = e^{\pi}.$$

The sum of (6) when $x = -\pi$ is, therefore, $\frac{1}{2}(e^{-\pi}+e^{\pi})$.

4. Sine series and cosine series

4.1. If $f(x)$ is an even† function of x, then

$$\int\limits_{-\pi}^{\pi} f(x)\sin mx\,dx = 0$$

and the Fourier series of $f(x)$ is a series of cosines only.

Similarly, if $f(x)$ is an odd function of x, then its Fourier series is one of sines only.

4.2. We can find series of sines or cosines, as we wish, that are related to a given function $f(x)$ in $(0, \pi)$, though not necessarily so related outside this interval.

Take any function $f(x)$ that is integrable in $(0, \pi)$ and define two new functions thus:

in $0 \leqslant x \leqslant \pi$,   let $\phi(x) = f(x)$, $\psi(x) = f(x)$;

in $-\pi < x < 0$,   let $\phi(x) = f(-x)$, $\psi(x) = -f(-x)$;

for other values of x let ϕ, ψ be defined by the periodicity equations $\phi(x+2\pi) = \phi(x)$, $\psi(x+2\pi) = \psi(x)$.

Then the Fourier series of the even function $\phi(x)$ is

$$\tfrac{1}{2}a_0 + \sum_{n=1}^{\infty} a_n \cos nx, \qquad (7)$$

where $\quad \pi a_k = \int\limits_{-\pi}^{\pi} \phi(x)\cos kx\,dx = 2\int\limits_{0}^{\pi} f(x)\cos kx\,dx.$

Assuming the Fourier series of $\phi(x)$ to be convergent, its sum will be $\tfrac{1}{2}\{\phi(x+0)+\phi(x-0)\}$ when these two limits exist. This sum is:

for $0 < x < \pi$, $\tfrac{1}{2}\{f(x+0)+f(x-0)\}$;

for $x = 0$, $\tfrac{1}{2}\{f(+0)+f(+0)\}$ i.e. $f(+0)$;

for $x = \pi$, $\tfrac{1}{2}\{f(\pi-0)+f(\pi-0)\}$ i.e. $f(\pi-0)$.

For other values of x the sum is related to $\phi(x)$ and not to $f(x)$.

† DEFINITION. $f(x)$ is an even function of x if $f(-x) = f(x)$;
        $f(x)$ is an odd function of x if $f(-x) = -f(x)$.
When $f(x)$ is an even function,

$$\int\limits_{-\pi}^{\pi} f(x)\sin mx\,dx = \int\limits_{0}^{\pi} f(x)\sin mx\,dx - \int\limits_{0}^{\pi} f(t)\sin mt\,dt = 0,$$

as we see by putting $t = -x$ in the interval $-\pi < x < 0$.

The Fourier series of the odd function $\psi(x)$ is

$$\sum_{n=1}^{\infty} b_n \sin nx, \tag{8}$$

where $\qquad \pi b_k = \int_{-\pi}^{\pi} \psi(x)\sin kx\, dx = 2\int_0^{\pi} f(x)\sin kx\, dx.$

The function $\frac{1}{2}\{\psi(x+0)+\psi(x-0)\}$ is $\frac{1}{2}\{f(x+0)+f(x-0)\}$ when $0 < x < \pi$.

When $x = 0, \pi$ the sum of (8) is clearly zero. For values of x outside $(0,\pi)$ the series is related to $\psi(x)$ and not necessarily to $f(x)$.

4.3. *A worked example. To find the series of sines that represents* x^2 *in* $0 < x < \pi$.

Let $\qquad f(x) = x^2 \qquad$ when $\quad 0 \leqslant x \leqslant \pi,$

$\qquad\qquad\quad f(x) = -x^2 \quad$ when $-\pi < x < 0,$

and let $f(x)$ be defined by the periodicity equation

$$f(x+2\pi) = f(x)$$

for values of x other than $-\pi < x \leqslant \pi$.

The Fourier coefficients of $f(x)$ are given by

$$a_n = 0, \quad \text{since } f(x) \text{ is an odd function,}$$

$$\pi b_n = 2\int_0^{\pi} x^2 \sin nx\, dx$$

$$= \frac{2\pi^2(-1)^{n+1}}{n} + \frac{4}{n^3}\{(-1)^n - 1\}. \tag{9}$$

The Fourier series of $f(x)$ is $\sum b_n \sin nx$, where b_n is defined by (9). This series is convergent (Chap. IX, §3.5 proves $\sum (-1)^{n+1}n^{-1}\sin nx$ to be convergent) and its sum is $\frac{1}{2}\{f(x+0)+f(x-0)\}$.

When $0 < x < \pi$, $f(x+0) = f(x-0) = x^2$, and so the sum of the series is x^2.

When $x = 0$ or π the sum is zero: outside $(0,\pi)$ the series does not represent x^2.

5. Intervals other than $(-\pi, \pi)$

5.1. If we require a Fourier series to represent $f(x)$ in $(0, 2\pi)$ we proceed as in §3.5, but we use $(0, 2\pi)$ instead of

$(-\pi, \pi)$. Thus, to represent x in the interval $(0, 2\pi)$ we calculate

$$a_0 = \frac{1}{\pi} \int_0^{2\pi} x \, dx, \qquad a_n = \frac{1}{\pi} \int_0^{2\pi} x \cos nx \, dx,$$

$$b_n = \frac{1}{\pi} \int_0^{2\pi} x \sin nx \, dx,$$

and so obtain

$$x = \pi - 2 \sum_{n=1}^{\infty} \frac{\sin nx}{n} \quad (0 < x < 2\pi).$$

5.2. We can make the interval (a, b) correspond to the interval $(-\pi, \pi)$ by means of the transformation

$$\frac{x-a}{b-a} = \frac{X+\pi}{2\pi},$$

i.e.

$$X = \frac{2\pi x - \pi(a+b)}{b-a}.$$

To represent $f(x)$ by a Fourier series in (a, b), let $f(x) \equiv F(X)$ and let

$$\pi a_k = \int_{-\pi}^{\pi} F(t) \cos kt \, dt$$

$$= \frac{2\pi}{b-a} \int_a^b f(\theta) \cos \frac{\pi k(2\theta - a - b)}{b-a} \, d\theta,$$

$$\pi b_k = \int_{-\pi}^{\pi} F(t) \sin kt \, dt$$

$$= \frac{2\pi}{b-a} \int_a^b f(\theta) \sin \frac{\pi k(2\theta - a - b)}{b-a} \, d\theta.$$

Then, assuming the convergence of the series and the existence of the limits, we find that

$$\tfrac{1}{2}a_0 + \sum_{n=1}^{\infty} (a_n \cos nX + b_n \sin nX)$$

represents $\frac{1}{2}\{F(X+0) + F(X-0)\}$ in $-\pi < X < \pi$; and so

$$\tfrac{1}{2}a_0 + \sum_{n=1}^{\infty} \left[a_n \cos \frac{n\pi}{b-a}(2x-a-b) + b_n \sin \frac{n\pi}{b-a}(2x-a-b) \right]$$

represents $\frac{1}{2}\{f(x+0) + f(x-0\}$ in $a < x < b$.

6. Proof of Theorem 65

6.1. THEOREM 65 A. *Let $|f(x)|$ be integrable in $(-\pi, \pi)$ and let $f(x)$ have a period 2π; let*

$$\pi a_k = \int_{-\pi}^{\pi} f(t)\cos kt\, dt, \qquad \pi b_k = \int_{-\pi}^{\pi} f(t)\sin kt\, dt, \qquad (1)$$

$$s_n = \tfrac{1}{2}a_0 + \sum_{m=1}^{n}(a_m \cos mx + b_m \sin mx), \qquad (2)$$

and let
$$\sigma_n = \frac{s_0 + s_1 + \ldots + s_{n-1}}{n}. \qquad (3)$$

Then, for any x such that the limits $f(x+0), f(x-0)$ are defined,
$$\sigma_n \to \tfrac{1}{2}\{f(x+0) + f(x-0)\}. \qquad (4)$$

First step. By (1) and (2),

$$s_n = \frac{1}{2\pi}\int_{-\pi}^{\pi} f(t)\, dt + \frac{1}{\pi}\sum_{m=1}^{n}\int_{-\pi}^{\pi} \cos m(x-t)f(t)\, dt$$

$$= \frac{1}{2\pi}\int_{-\pi}^{\pi} \frac{\sin\{(n+\tfrac{1}{2})(x-t)\}}{\sin\tfrac{1}{2}(x-t)} f(t)\, dt,$$

on summing the series $\tfrac{1}{2} + \cos(x-t) + \ldots + \cos n(x-t)$.

Now put $t - x = u$; we get

$$s_n = \frac{1}{2\pi}\int_{-\pi-x}^{\pi-x} \frac{\sin(n+\tfrac{1}{2})u}{\sin\tfrac{1}{2}u} f(u+x)\, du.$$

But the integrand has a period 2π, and so its values from $-\pi-x$ to $-\pi$ are repeated in its values from $\pi-x$ to π. Hence

$$s_n = \frac{1}{2\pi}\int_{-\pi}^{\pi} \frac{\sin(n+\tfrac{1}{2})u}{\sin\tfrac{1}{2}u} f(u+x)\, du$$

$$= \frac{1}{2\pi}\int_{0}^{\pi} \frac{\sin(n+\tfrac{1}{2})u}{\sin\tfrac{1}{2}u}\{f(x+u) + f(x-u)\}\, du,$$

on writing $-u$ for u in $(-\pi, 0)$.

On summing $\sin\tfrac{1}{2}u+\sin\tfrac{3}{2}u+\ldots+\sin\tfrac{1}{2}(2n-1)u$, we get

$$\sigma_n = \frac{1}{2n\pi} \int_0^\pi \frac{\sin^2\tfrac{1}{2}nu}{\sin^2\tfrac{1}{2}u}\{f(x+u)+f(x-u)\}\,du. \tag{5}$$

But we also have, on taking the particular case $f(x) \equiv 1$ (when $a_0 = 2$ is the only Fourier coefficient that does not vanish, and so $s_n \equiv 1$ and $\sigma_n \equiv 1$),

$$1 = \frac{1}{2n\pi} \int_0^\pi \frac{\sin^2\tfrac{1}{2}nu}{\sin^2\tfrac{1}{2}u}\,2\,du. \tag{6}$$

If s is any given number, then, by (5) and (6),

$$\sigma_n - s = \frac{1}{2n\pi} \int_0^\pi \frac{\sin^2\tfrac{1}{2}nu}{\sin^2\tfrac{1}{2}u}\phi(u)\,du, \tag{7}$$

where
$$\phi(u) = f(x+u)+f(x-u)-2s. \tag{8}$$

PARENTHESIS. What we have to prove is that (7) will tend to zero as n tends to infinity if we take s to be $\tfrac{1}{2}\{f(x+0)+f(x-0)\}$. The first step has been concerned solely with arriving at a suitable form for $\sigma_n - s$.

Second step. Let δ be any fixed positive number less than π. Then

$$\left| \frac{1}{n} \int_\delta^\pi \frac{\sin^2\tfrac{1}{2}nu}{\sin^2\tfrac{1}{2}u}\phi(u)\,du \right| \leqslant \frac{1}{n}\operatorname{cosec}^2\tfrac{1}{2}\delta \int_\delta^\pi |\phi(u)|\,du. \tag{9}$$

By hypothesis, $|f(x)|$ is integrable, and so the integral on the right of (9) is a finite number, independent of n. Hence (9) tends to zero as n tends to infinity.

This disposes of the interval (δ, π). We begin our attack on the interval $(0, \delta)$ by noting that

$$\operatorname{cosec}^2\tfrac{1}{2}u-(\tfrac{1}{2}u)^{-2}$$

is bounded in $(0, \delta)$ (expand $(\sin\tfrac{1}{2}u)^{-2}$ and use the analogue of Chap. XV, §4). It follows that

$$\left| \frac{1}{n} \int_0^\delta \sin^2\tfrac{1}{2}nu\left\{\frac{1}{\sin^2\tfrac{1}{2}u}-\frac{1}{(\tfrac{1}{2}u)^2}\right\}\phi(u)\,du \right| \leqslant \frac{1}{n} \int_0^\delta K|\phi(u)|\,du \to 0.$$

But the expression (9) also tends to zero, so that (7) will tend to zero if, with a definite positive δ less than π,

$$\frac{1}{n} \int_0^\delta \frac{\sin^2\frac{1}{2}nu}{u^2} \phi(u) \, du \to 0. \tag{10}$$

Third step. Suppose now that x is a value for which

$$\tfrac{1}{2}\{f(x+0)+f(x-0)\}$$

is defined—i.e. the limits exist—and put $s = \tfrac{1}{2}\{f(x+0)+f(x-0)\}$. Then

$$\phi(u) = f(x+u)+f(x-u)-f(x+0)-f(x-0),$$

so that, by the definition of $\phi(u)$, $\phi(u) \to 0$ as $u \to 0$. Hence

$$\epsilon > 0, \, A > 0; \; \exists \; \eta \; . \; |\phi(u)| < \epsilon/A \quad \text{when } |u| < \eta.$$

We now take a definite η, choosing it to be less than δ. Then, for all n,

$$\left| \frac{1}{n} \int_0^\delta \frac{\sin^2\frac{1}{2}nu}{u^2} \phi(u) \, du \right|$$

$$\leqslant \frac{\epsilon}{An} \int_0^\eta \frac{\sin^2\frac{1}{2}nu}{u^2} \, du + \frac{1}{n} \int_\eta^\delta \frac{\sin^2\frac{1}{2}nu}{u^2} |\phi(u)| \, du$$

$$= I_1 + I_2,$$

say. But, on putting $v = \tfrac{1}{2}nu$ in the first integral,

$$\frac{1}{n} \int_0^\eta \frac{\sin^2\frac{1}{2}nu}{u^2} \, du = \frac{1}{2} \int_0^{\frac{1}{2}n\eta} \frac{\sin^2 v}{v^2} \, dv < \frac{1}{2} \int_0^\infty \frac{\sin^2 v}{v^2} \, dv,$$

which is a positive constant; if we take

$$A = \int_0^\infty \frac{\sin^2 v}{v^2} \, dv,$$

we have, at this point, $0 < I_1 < \tfrac{1}{2}\epsilon$.

Again, $$0 < I_2 \leqslant \frac{1}{n} \int_\eta^\delta \frac{|\phi(u)|}{u^2} \, du,$$

$$< n^{-1}\eta^{-2} \int_\eta^\delta |\phi(u)| \, du.$$

Since η, δ are fixed, we can find an N for which

$$0 < I_2 < \tfrac{1}{2}\epsilon \quad \text{when } n \geqslant N.$$

Hence

$$\epsilon > 0; \quad \exists \ N \ . \ \left| \frac{1}{n} \int_0^\delta \frac{\sin^2\tfrac{1}{2}nu}{u^2} \phi(u) \, du \right| < \epsilon \quad \text{when } n \geqslant N.$$

That is, (10) is true and, by the second step, (7) $\to 0$ as $n \to \infty$; that is,

$$\sigma_n \to \tfrac{1}{2}\{f(x+0)+f(x-0)\}.$$

6.2. If, further, s_n tends to a finite limit, that is, if the series

$$\tfrac{1}{2}a_0 + \sum_{m=1}^{\infty} (a_m \cos mx + b_m \sin mx)$$

is convergent, then (Theorem 63) σ_n tends to the same limit as does s_n. Hence Theorem 65 follows from Theorem 65 A.

EXAMPLES XXV

1. Prove that

$$\frac{\pi-x}{2} = \frac{\sin x}{1} + \frac{\sin 2x}{2} + \frac{\sin 3x}{3} + \ldots \quad (0 < x < 2\pi).$$

2. Prove that the function $f(\theta)$, where

$$f(\theta) = \tfrac{1}{2}\theta(\pi-\alpha) \quad \text{when } -\alpha \leqslant \theta \leqslant \alpha \ (<\pi),$$
$$f(\theta) = \tfrac{1}{2}\alpha(\pi-\theta) \quad \text{when } \quad \alpha \leqslant \theta \leqslant 2\pi-\alpha,$$

can be represented in $(-\alpha, 2\pi-\alpha)$ by the series

$$\sum n^{-2} \sin n\theta \sin n\alpha.$$

3. Prove that, when $0 \leqslant x < \pi$,

$$x = \frac{1}{2}\pi - \frac{4}{\pi}\left(\cos x + \frac{1}{3^2}\cos 3x + \frac{1}{5^2}\cos 5x + \ldots\right).$$

4. Find the cosine series that represents x^2 in $(-\pi, \pi)$.

5. Show that $\sum b_n \sin nx$, where

$$b_n = -\frac{8}{3n}\cos\frac{n\pi}{2}\sin\frac{n\pi}{3}\sin\frac{n\pi}{6}$$

represents in $(0, \pi)$ the function $\tfrac{1}{2}\{f(x+0)+f(x-0)\}$, where $f(x)$ is $\tfrac{1}{3}\pi$ when $0 < x < \tfrac{1}{3}\pi$, is zero when $\tfrac{1}{3}\pi < x < \tfrac{2}{3}\pi$, and is $-\tfrac{1}{3}\pi$ when $\tfrac{2}{3}\pi < x < \pi$.

6. Prove that, in $-\pi < x < \pi$,

$$x+x^2 = \tfrac{1}{3}\pi^2 + 4(-\cos x + \tfrac{1}{2}\sin x) + (\cos 2x - \sin 2x) + \ldots.$$

7. Prove that, if $-\pi < x < \pi$, then

$$\pi^2 - x^2 = \tfrac{2}{3}\pi^2 + 4(\cos x - \tfrac{1}{4}\cos 2x + \tfrac{1}{9}\cos 3x - \ldots).$$

MISCELLANEOUS EXAMPLES

1. Prove that $\sum n^k z^n$ is convergent when $|z| < 1$. If $F_k(z)$ is its sum, show that

$$F_{k+1}(z) = z\frac{d}{dz}F_k(z)$$

and that, when k is a positive integer,

$$F_k(z) = \sum_{r=0}^{k} \frac{(-)^r A_r}{(1-z)^{k-r+1}},$$

where the A_r are *positive* constants. (Use induction.)

2. From the formula

$$\frac{n\sin n\theta}{\cos n\theta - 1} = \sum_{r=0}^{n-1} \frac{\sin\theta}{\cos\theta - \cos 2r\alpha},$$

where $\alpha = \pi/n$, deduce that

$$\tfrac{1}{3}(n^2-1) = \sum_{r=1}^{n-1} \operatorname{cosec}^2 r\alpha.$$

3. Given that $\sum a_n$ is a divergent series of positive terms, show that $\sum a_n/(1+n^2 a_n)$ is convergent and $\sum a_n/(1+a_n)$ is divergent.

4. Show that the double series

$$\sum\sum \frac{(m+n)!}{m!\,n!}(\tfrac{1}{2}x)^{m+n} \quad (m, n = 0, 1, 2,...)$$

converges by rows or by columns to $(1-x)^{-1}$ provided that $-2 < x < 1$.

5. The series $\sum a_n$ is convergent, and

$$b_n = \frac{a_n}{n+1} + \frac{a_{n+1}}{n+2} + \dots.$$

Transform b_n by Abel's identity (sum the a's, and difference the $1/(n+r)$; see p. 62) and prove that $nb_n \to 0$ as $n \to \infty$.

Show further that, if $B_n = b_0 + b_1 + \dots + b_n$, $A_n = a_0 + a_1 + \dots + a_n$, then $A_n = B_n - (n+1)b_{n+1}$; and hence show that $\sum b_n = \sum a_n$.

6. Discuss, for all real values of x, the convergence, and in particular the ranges of uniform convergence, of

$$\sum n^{-1}(1+x^n)^{-1}(-x)^n.$$

7. Find the sums of the series

$$\sum_{n=1}^{\infty} (9n^3-n)^{-1}, \qquad \sum_{n=0}^{\infty} \{(n+1)(2n+1)\}^{-1}.$$

8. If $y+y^{-1} = \xi+i\eta$, prove that $\{(1-ty)(1-ty^{-1})\}^{-\frac{1}{2}}$ may be expanded as a power series in t convergent when $|t| < \omega$, where $0 < \omega < 1$, provided that the point (ξ, η) lies either on the ellipse

$$\frac{\xi^2}{(\omega+\omega^{-1})^2} + \frac{\eta^2}{(\omega^{-1}-\omega)^2} = 1,$$

or inside this ellipse.

9. If a_n is m.d. and $\to 0$, and if $\phi(n) = O(n^k)$, prove that the convergence of $\sum |a_n \phi(n)|$ implies $n^{k+1} a_n \to 0$. (Compare Pringsheim's theorem, Examples VIII, 12.)

10. If $\sum a_n x^n$ is absolutely convergent when $|x| \leqslant R$ and $R > 0$, show that $\sum a_n x^n/n!$ converges for all values of x.

11. Find the radius of convergence of the power series

$$\sum \frac{1 \cdot 3 \ldots (2n-1)}{2 \cdot 4 \ldots 2n}\left(1 + \frac{1}{2} + \ldots + \frac{1}{n}\right) x^{2n}$$

and discuss the behaviour of the series *on* its circle of convergence.

12. Prove, by using partial fractions or by any other method, that

$$\frac{1 - r\cos\theta}{1 - 2r\cos\theta + r^2} = 1 + r\cos\theta + r^2\cos 2\theta + \ldots \quad (|r| < 1),$$

$$\frac{1 - r^2}{1 - 2r\cos\theta + r^2} = 1 + 2r\cos\theta + 2r^2\cos 2\theta + \ldots \quad (|r| < 1),$$

$$\frac{r\sin\theta}{1 - 2r\cos\theta + r^2} = r\sin\theta + r^2\sin 2\theta + \ldots \quad (|r| < 1).$$

$$[(1 - 2r\cos\theta + r^2) = (1 - re^{i\theta})(1 - re^{-i\theta}).]$$

13. Find the series of cosines that represents

$$\frac{d}{dr}\log(1 - 2r\cos\theta + r^2),$$

and hence prove that

$$-\tfrac{1}{2}\log(1 - 2r\cos\theta + r^2) = r\cos\theta + \tfrac{1}{2}r^2\cos 2\theta + \ldots \quad (|r| < 1).$$

14. Use 13 and Abel's theorem to prove that, when $0 < \theta < 2\pi$,

$$\cos\theta + \tfrac{1}{2}\cos 2\theta + \tfrac{1}{3}\cos 3\theta + \ldots = -\log(2\sin\tfrac{1}{2}\theta).$$

15. When $|x| < 1$, prove that

$$\tfrac{1}{2}\log(1 + 2x\sin\theta + x^2) = x\sin\theta + \tfrac{1}{2}x^2\cos 2\theta - \tfrac{1}{3}x^3\sin 3\theta - \ldots.$$

Prove that, when n is a positive odd integer,

$$\frac{\sin n\theta}{\sin\theta} = n - \frac{n(n^2-1^2)}{3!}\sin^2\theta + \frac{n(n^2-1^2)(n^2-3^2)}{5!}\sin^4\theta - \ldots.$$

16. If $\sum nc_n$ is convergent, then so is

$$c_n + 2c_{n+1} + 3c_{n+2} + \ldots,$$

and its sum $\to 0$ as $n \to \infty$.

17. Prove that, in the usual binomial coefficient notation,

$$\binom{2n}{0}^2 - \binom{2n}{1}^2 + \ldots + \binom{2n}{2n}^2 = (-1)^n\binom{2n}{n},$$

$$\binom{n}{1} - \frac{1}{2}\binom{n}{2} + \ldots + (-)^{n-1}\frac{1}{n}\binom{n}{n} = 1 + \frac{1}{2} + \frac{1}{3} + \ldots + \frac{1}{n}.$$

18. Prove that
$$y = 1+\left(\frac{1}{2}\right)^2 x+\left(\frac{1.3}{2.4}\right)^2 x^2+...+\left(\frac{1.3...2n-1}{2.4...2n}\right)^2 x^n+...$$
satisfies the differential equation
$$x(1-x)\frac{d^2y}{dx^2}+(1-2x)\frac{dy}{dx}-\tfrac{1}{4}y = 0,$$
and find the radius of convergence of the series that defines y.

19. Prove   that $1-\tfrac{1}{2}+\tfrac{1}{4}-\tfrac{1}{8}+...$, $1-\tfrac{1}{2}-\tfrac{1}{2}+\tfrac{1}{4}+\tfrac{1}{4}+\tfrac{1}{4}-\tfrac{1}{8}-...$ (the series containing blocks of 1, 2, 3, 4,... equal terms) are convergent series; but that
$$1-\tfrac{1}{2}-\tfrac{1}{2}+\tfrac{1}{4}+\tfrac{1}{4}+\tfrac{1}{4}+\tfrac{1}{4}-\tfrac{1}{8}-...$$
(with blocks of 1, 2, 4, 8,... equal terms) is not convergent.

20. If $b > 0$ and $\sum x_n^{-1}$ is a divergent series of positive terms, prove that
$$\frac{1}{b}-\frac{1}{x_1}-\sum_{n=1}^{p}\frac{(x_1-b)(x_2-b)...(x_n-b)}{x_1 x_2... x_{n+1}} = \frac{(x_1-b)...(x_{p+1}-b)}{bx_1 x_2... x_{p+1}},$$
$$\frac{1}{b}-\frac{1}{x_1} = \sum_{n=1}^{\infty}\frac{(x_1-b)...(x_n-b)}{x_1 x_2... x_{n+1}}.$$

21. The function $f(x)$ is defined by
$$f(x) = \sum_{n=0}^{\infty}\frac{(ix)^n}{n!}.$$
Deduce from the series, and without quoting properties of trigonometrical functions, that

(i) $f(x)f(y) = f(x+y)$,   (ii) $|f(x)| = 1$,   (iii) $\dfrac{d}{dx}\arg f(x) = 1$.

Prove that $f(x)$ is a periodic function of x.

[NOTE: $|a+ib|^2 = (a+ib)(a-ib)$.]

22. Use   the   inequality $(\sum a_n b_n)^2 \leqslant (\sum a_n^2)(\sum b_n^2)$ to   show   that $\displaystyle\sum_{n=-\infty}^{\infty} a_n b_{n-k}$ is convergent when $\displaystyle\sum_{n=-\infty}^{\infty} a_n^2$, $\displaystyle\sum_{n=-\infty}^{\infty} b_n^2$ are convergent. Prove that its sum $\to 0$ as $k \to \infty$.

23. The number of sets of values of $m_1, m_2,..., m_k$ (integers not all zero) whose absolute value $\leqslant x$ is $(2x+1)^k-1$. The number of sets where these absolute values $< x$ is $(2x-1)^k-1$. (The m's may be positive or negative.) If $S = \sum (m_1^2+m_2^2+...+m_k^2)^{-\alpha}$, a multiple sum, and S_x is the sum of the terms wherein at least one $|m|$ has the value x, then
$$\frac{(2x+1)^k-(2x-1)^k}{x^{2\alpha}} \geqslant S_x \geqslant \frac{1}{k^\alpha}\cdot\frac{(2x+1)^k-(2x-1)^k}{x^{2\alpha}}.$$
Hence show that S converges when $\displaystyle\sum_{x=1}^{\infty} x^{k-1-2\alpha}$ converges.

24. When n is a positive integer, prove that

$$\frac{x}{(1-x)(1-x^{2n+1})} + \frac{x^3}{(1-x^3)(1-x^{2n+3})} + \frac{x^5}{(1-x^5)(1-x^{2n+5})} + \cdots$$

is $\dfrac{1}{1-x^{2n}}\left\{\dfrac{x}{1-x} + \dfrac{x^3}{1-x^3} + \cdots + \dfrac{x^{2n-1}}{1-x^{2n-1}}\right\}$ if $|x| < 1$

and is $\dfrac{1}{1-x^{2n}}\left\{\dfrac{1}{1-x} + \dfrac{1}{1-x^3} + \cdots + \dfrac{1}{1-x^{2n-1}}\right\}$ if $|x| > 1$.

25. Show that the series

$$\sum_{n=1}^{\infty} \frac{z^{n-1}}{(1-z^n)(1-z^{n+1})}$$

is equal to $(1-z)^{-2}$ when $|z| < 1$ and is equal to $z^{-1}(1-z)^{-2}$ when $|z| > 1$.

26.† $F(z) \equiv$

$$\frac{z}{(1-q)(1-z)} + \frac{(1-q)z^2}{(1-q^2)(1-z)(1-qz)} + \frac{(1-q)(1-q^2)z^3}{(1-q^3)(1-z)(1-qz)(1-q^2z)} + \cdots,$$

where $|z| < 1$ and $|q| < 1$. Show that

$F(z) - F(qz) =$

$$\frac{z}{1-z}\left\{\frac{1}{1-qz} + \frac{(1-q)z}{(1-qz)(1-q^2z)} + \frac{(1-q)(1-q^2)z^2}{(1-qz)(1-q^2z)(1-q^3z)} + \cdots\right\}$$

$$= z(1-z)^{-2},$$

$$F(z) = z(1-z)^{-2} + qz(1-qz)^{-2} + \cdots$$

$$= \sum_{n=1}^{\infty} \frac{n}{1-q^n} z^n.$$

27. Differentiate the result of Example 26 with respect to z and put $z = q$, to obtain

$$\sum_{n=1}^{\infty} \frac{q^n}{(1-q^n)^2}\left\{\frac{1}{1-q} + \frac{1}{1-q^2} + \cdots + \frac{1}{1-q^n}\right\} = \sum_{n=1}^{\infty} \frac{n^2 q^n}{1-q^n}.$$

† Examples 26, 27 are taken from a paper by W. N. Bailey, *Journal London Math. Soc.* **11** (1936), 157.

APPENDIX

1. The definition of a real number, given in § 2, is abstruse and far removed from 'common sense'. Some such definition is a necessity and not a matter of choice. It is 'common sense' to suppose that some 'number' corresponds to each 'length' of line in a geometrical figure. In each of the two great constructive periods of mathematics this 'common-sense' view has been found unsatisfactory.

In the ancient period the Greeks found that

(*a*) their theory of numbers dealt only with integers and the ratio of integers;

(*b*) their geometry introduced lengths that could not be represented by such numbers, e.g. the diagonal of a unit square.

Their solution was to accept (*a*), to build up a geometrical theory of incommensurables, and to make all geometrical propositions independent of any results discovered by means of (*a*). For example, it is almost certain that Pythagoras' theorem was discovered by some variant of the argument

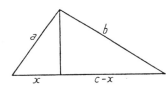

$$\text{`}\frac{x}{a} = \frac{a}{c}, \quad \frac{c-x}{b} = \frac{b}{c},$$

and so, on cross-multiplication and addition,

$$c^2 = a^2 + b^2\text{'}.$$

The proof usually given in Book I of Euclid (even in modern geometries!) is one that deliberately avoids arithmetical arguments.

In the modern period analysis reached the stage of very careful discussion of continuity, convergence, and so on, without any close examination of what it meant by an irrational number. Cauchy (p. 4 of *Cours d'Analyse*, 1821) merely says: 'an irrational number is the limit of diverse fractions which furnish more and more approximate values of it', and it is much later in the book that he builds up his technique of ϵ and N, now so familiar in the definition of what a limit is. That is, Cauchy takes the 'common-sense' view of what an irrational is and then builds up his theory of limits (in the strict mathematical sense) for both rational and irrational numbers. Later on, when people were familiar with the idea of limit in the strict mathematical sense, it was inevitable that some one should ask, 'what does limit mean on page 4 of Cauchy's *Cours d'Analyse*?' Whatever answer is given, the result is unsatisfactory: either 'limit' is used before it is defined, or the word 'limit' is used in two different ways, i.e. in the first instance it expresses a vague notion and not a definite one.

All attempts to build up a theory of limits, which shall be applicable both to rational and to irrational numbers, are bound to fail unless they are prefaced by an exact arithmetical definition of rational and irrational number.

Further, some of the work of 1800–60 showed that geometrical intuitions, though frequently useful and reliable as guides to analytical results, were not invariably so. Analysis sometimes deals with functions y, of a variable x, that cannot be represented graphically. Thus, cf. Goursat, *Cours d'Analyse*, i. 75,

$$y = \sum_{n=0}^{\infty} b^n \cos(a^n \pi x),$$

where $b < 1$ and a is an odd integer, has the properties

(i) it is a continuous function of x,

(ii) it has a differential coefficient if $ab < 1$, but not if $ab > 1 + \frac{3}{2}\pi$.

If $ab > 1 + \frac{3}{2}\pi$, then any notion of a graph or geometrical picture of the function is bound to be false: we cannot think of a graph that nowhere has a tangent.

The net result of the logical difficulties into which the older point of view had led is that modern analysis aims at being purely arithmetical: even when it deals with geometrical facts it deals with them in an arithmetical fashion.

NOTE. There is one important note to be made in this connexion. The arithmetical argument is often doing nothing more than state, in the requisite forms, facts which are indicated by geometry. It is frequently useful to draw a figure and see *what* geometrical intuitions are being arithmetized.

2. Real numbers

We shall assume the notions of

unity, aggregate or *set, order, correspondence.*

We shall assume that the theory of positive and negative integers and fractions has been developed and that rules for their comparison ($>, =, <$), their addition, subtraction, multiplication, and division have been given.† These are the rational numbers, or, to distinguish them from what we shall later call rational real numbers, the *elementary rational numbers* (E.R.)

Anent these, we notice three results that will be particularly useful.

(i) Any set of E.R. that contains 1 and is such that it must contain $k+1$ if it contains k contains the unending sequence $1, 2, 3, \dots$. This is called the *Principle of Mathematical Induction.*

(ii) If a, b are two positive E.R. and $a < b$, then we can find positive integers n such that $na > b$. This is sometimes called *Archimedes' Axiom* from the fact that Archimedes set it out in a form concerning lengths of lines.

(iii) If a is an E.R., then there is no least E.R. which exceeds a.

Proof. If b is *any* E.R. greater than a, then so is $\frac{1}{2}(a+b)$: it is less than b, and so b cannot be the least E.R. which exceeds a.

Dedekind cuts or sections

DEFINITION. *Two sets L, R of elementary rational numbers are said to form a cut when*

(a) *there is at least one E.R. in each set,*

(b) *each and every E.R. belongs either to L or to R, but not to both,*

(c) *each and every member of L < each and every member of R.*

A *real number* is a cut of the elementary rational numbers.

The notation (L, R) will be used to denote a cut; alternatively, in discussing particular cuts, a single letter or symbol, such as a, $\frac{1}{2}$, $\sqrt{2}$ will be used.

---

† Cf. Hobson, *Functions of a Real Variable*, vol. i (1921), pp. 1–18. Any one who is really interested in the logical foundations of analysis will find this well worth reading.

LEMMA. (L, R) *is a cut and a is an* E.R. *of* R: *then any* E.R. *b that exceeds a is also in* R.

Proof. If b is in L, then (c) of the definition is not satisfied.

Geometrical picture

If we think of the E.R. plotted along a line, a cut will be given if we take a point P on that line, put all E.R. to the left

in L, all to the right in R, and, in case P itself corresponds to an E.R., then that E.R. may be put either in L or in R, but not in both. The rough geometrical picture will help to keep clear the implications of the arithmetical arguments which come later.

Classification of real numbers

There are two simple types of cut which are, quite naturally, called *rational* real numbers.

(i) When L contains all E.R. $\leqslant$ a given E.R. a,

and $\qquad R$ contains all E.R. $> a$,

then the cut (L, R) is denoted by a and is called a rational real number. Occasionally, to avoid confusion, we shall use a' for the rational real number, a for the E.R.

(ii) When L contains all E.R. $<$ a given E.R. a,

and $\qquad R$ contains all E.R. $\geqslant a$,

then the cut (L, R) is denoted by a and is called a rational real number.

We shall refer to either of these cuts as the rational real number 'corresponding to the E.R. a' or 'derived from the E.R. a'.

NOTE. We ought strictly, at this point, to use different symbols to denote the cuts of (i) and (ii): we shall see later that, with our definition of 'equals', the two real numbers or cuts (i) and (ii) are 'equal' when they are derived from one and the same E.R. a.

The chief characteristic to be noticed about (i) and (ii) before we proceed is that in them either L has a greatest member or R has a least.

We now ask 'Can we have cuts either

(iii) such that L has a greatest and R a least member, or

(iv) such that L has no greatest and R no least member?'

We see at once that the type (iii) is not possible. If possible, let α be the greatest L and β the least R; then $\frac{1}{2}(\alpha+\beta)$ lies between the two: being an E.R., it belongs either to L or to R if (L, R) is a cut. It follows that either β is not the least R or α is not the greatest L.

On the other hand, we have only to consider the cut that is indicated as the obvious way of defining $\sqrt{2}$ to see that type (iv) is possible. Define two sets L, R of E.R. in the following way:

every negative E.R. and

$$\left.\begin{array}{l} \text{every positive E.R. whose square} < 2 \text{ belongs to } L, \\ \text{every positive E.R. whose square} > 2 \text{ belongs to } R. \end{array}\right\} \text{(A)}$$

We want to show that (L, R) is a cut. To do this we have to show that the conditions (a), (b), (c) are satisfied. Now it is clear at once from (A) that (a) there is at least one E.R. in each of L and R and that (c) each and every member of $L <$ each and every member of R. Further, provided that there is no E.R. whose square is actually equal to 2, each and every E.R. belongs either to L or to R, but not to both.

Hence all we need do to show that L, R give a cut is to show that there is no elementary rational number whose square is 2. This was shown by the Greeks at the time when they encountered the logical difficulty referred to in § 1. Many proofs are known both of this and of such theorems as 'There is no rational number whose square is m/n (where this fraction is expressed in its lowest terms) unless m and n are the squares of integers'. There is some interest, however, in recalling the traditional Greek proof. In geometrical guise (i.e. it used lengths of lines) it ran on the following lines: *If $x:y$ is a ratio in its lowest terms, then its square cannot be 2.*

For if $x^2 = 2y^2$, then x^2 is even and, since the square of every odd number is odd, x is even. But now two things follow:

(i) since x, y have no common factor, y is odd;

(ii) since x is even, x^2 contains 4 as a factor; so y^2 is even, and y is also even because the square of every odd number is odd.

Hence y is both even and odd, which is absurd.

We now show that the cut given by (A) is one in which L has no least, R no greatest member. Let x be any E.R. in L and let $x^2 = 2-k$, where $k > 0$. If ϵ is a positive E.R. such that

$$\epsilon < x, \qquad \epsilon < k/3x,$$

then

$$(x+\epsilon)^2 = 2-k+2x\epsilon+\epsilon^2$$
$$= 2-k+\epsilon(2x+\epsilon)$$
$$< 2-k+\frac{k}{3x}3x,$$

and so $x+\epsilon$ also belongs to L. Hence x cannot be the greatest member of L.

Hence L has no greatest, and similarly R has no least, member.

IRRATIONAL NUMBERS. We have just established two facts:

(i) there is no cut (L, R) having a greatest member in L and a least member in R;

(ii) it is possible to have a cut (L, R) in which L has no greatest and R no least member.

DEFINITION. *A cut (L, R) in which L has no greatest and R no least member is called an irrational real number.*

3. The comparison of real numbers

Suppose two numbers a, b are given by cuts, say (L_1, R_1), (L_2, R_2). We use 'number' to denote 'real number' unless E.R. is expressly mentioned in the context.

For convenience, we shall use l_1 to denote any particular E.R. that belongs to L_1, and so on. Sometimes we use the phrase 'an l of a' instead of l_1.

The symbols $>$, $=$, $<$ between real numbers.

Either (i) all r's of $a \geqslant$ all l's of b,

or (ii) some r of $a <$ some l of b; when we say $a < b$.

When (i) holds, then

either (i a) some l of a > some r of b; when we say $a > b$,

or   (i b) all l's of a ≤ all r's of b; when we say $a = b$.

In (i b) it may happen that a and b are rational and that the greatest l of a = the least r of b, i.e. the cuts are the same save that in one the E.R. corresponding to the real number goes into L and in the other it goes into R.

NOTE. Draw a figure to see how obvious the above procedure is.

Positive and negative real numbers

Positive numbers are those that are greater than zero, negative numbers are those that are less than zero, zero (as a *real* number) being defined as the cut that has positive E.R. in its R class and negative E.R. in its L class. (Positive E.R. refers to what is meant by positive in the domain of the elementary rational numbers.)

Exercise. If x is a positive real number, then some l's of x are positive E.R.

DEFINITION. *If x denotes the cut (L, R), then $-x$ is denoted symbolically by $(-R, -L)$; if the E.R. c is an r of x, $-c$ is an l of $-x$, and if the E.R. c is an l of x, $-c$ is an r of $-x$.*

There is one concluding result that will exercise the reader in thinking about these definitions; it will be used in Theorem II. It is

'*If a, b are E.R. and $a > b$, and if a', b' are the rational real numbers derived from them, then, in the sense in which $>$ is defined for real numbers, $a' > b'$.*'

4. Operations with real numbers

THEOREM I. *Given an arbitrary E.R. $\epsilon > 0$, we can find, for any given cut (L, R), an l and an r such that $r-l < \epsilon$.*

If the cut (L, R) is a rational real number, the theorem is all but obvious. For then either L has a greatest member, say l_1, and $l_1+\frac{1}{2}\epsilon$ is necessarily an R, or R has a least, say r_1, and $r_1-\frac{1}{2}\epsilon$ is an L.

If the cut (L, R) is an irrational real number, let l_1 be any l and r_1 any r: let $r_1 - l_1 = \alpha$. Either $\alpha \leqslant \frac{1}{2}\epsilon$ and l_1, r_1 are numbers which satisfy $l_1 - r_1 < \epsilon$ or, by Archimedes' axiom, we can find an integer n such that $\frac{1}{2}\epsilon n > \alpha$. In the latter case, consider the $n+1$ E.R.

$$l_1, \quad l_1 + \tfrac{1}{2}\epsilon, \quad ..., \quad l_1 + \tfrac{1}{2}n\epsilon.$$

The last exceeds r_1 and so is in R; the first is in L; each must be either in L or in R, since each is an E.R. Hence one of the sequence is the last to be in L and the next is the first to be in R: their difference is $\frac{1}{2}\epsilon$ and we have found an l and an r such that $r - l < \epsilon$.

NOTE. The theorem is 'obvious' from the geometrical picture of §2.

The sum of real numbers

Let x, y denote the real numbers or cuts (L_1, R_1), (L_2, R_2). Divide the E.R. into two sets λ, ρ in this way: an E.R. c belongs to λ if we can find an l_1 and an l_2 such that

$$l_1 + l_2 \geqslant c;$$

otherwise c belongs to ρ.

Then, examining the conditions for a cut, we see that (b) each E.R. is either a λ or a ρ number, and (c) each and every member of $\lambda <$ each and every member of ρ.

The one thing needed to prove that (λ, ρ) is a cut is to show that there is at least one E.R. belonging to λ and at least one to ρ. To show this, take

k_1 other than the greatest member of L_1

(if there is such a greatest),

k_2 other than the greatest member of L_2

(if there is such a greatest).

Then, if $c = k_1 + k_2$, we can find an l_1 and an l_2 such that $l_1 + l_2 > c$: hence this c belongs to λ.

Moreover, any c of the form $r_1 + r_2$ belongs to ρ.

Hence (λ, ρ) is a cut; it is called the sum of x and y and is written $x + y$.

An alternative method of defining $x + y$ is given in Whittaker and Watson's *Modern Analysis* (pp. 5, 6): it is more intuitive, but leads to minor difficulties of detail.

A COROLLARY TO THE DEFINITION OF SUM. *If y is positive, then λ (above) contains* E.R. *that exceed* SOME *of the* E.R. *of R_1.*

$$\overline{}$$
　0　　　$\overset{\shortmid}{y}$　　　　　　　　　　$\overset{\shortmid}{x}$　　$\overset{\shortmid}{x{+}y}$

This result, needed for future reference, is geometrically obvious. The arithmetic proof is as follows:

Since $y > 0$, L_2 contains *some* positive E.R. If l_2 is one such, then, by Theorem I, we can find an l_1 and an r_1 such that

$$r_1 < l_1 + l_2.$$

Moreover, $l_1 + l_2$ is a member of λ.

THE DIFFERENCE OF REAL NUMBERS. *The number $x - y$ is defined to be $x + (-y)$.*

The product of real numbers

In the first place, suppose x and y to be positive real numbers. We then proceed much as we did in defining a sum; put the E.R. c in L if we can find a positive l_1 and a positive l_2 such that $l_1 l_2 \geqslant c$; otherwise put c in R. Then (L, R) may be proved to be a cut, called the product of x and y, and written xy.

If x or y (or both) is negative, then we frame the definition so that the familiar 'rule of signs' for elementary rational numbers will still hold for real numbers; e.g. if x is negative and y is positive, then xy is defined as $-(-x)y$.

THE RECIPROCAL OF A NUMBER. *If x denotes the positive number (L, R), then its reciprocal, $1/x$, is the number (L_1, R_1), where R_1 consists of the reciprocals of all positive l's of x and L_1 of all* E.R. *that are not reciprocals of positive l's of x.*

If x denotes a negative number, then $1/x$ is defined to be $-(1/-x)$.

FURTHER OPERATIONS. Division by x is multiplication by $(1/x)$. The reader can, if he so wishes, fill in the details of defining x^n (n an integer), $\sqrt[n]{x}$, etc. The details present no difficulty, though some care will be necessary.

5. The manipulation of real numbers

To make a complete preparation for manipulating real numbers with the same confidence as we did before the abstract definition by means of cuts was known to us, we ought at this stage to set up a lengthy formal scheme. For example, the proposition $\frac{1}{2}a < a$ when $a > 0$, though easily proved, is not so obvious that it can be dismissed as silly when we are discussing real numbers. Again, the theorems in proportion must be proved for real numbers, e.g. if $a/b = c/d$ then $ad = bc$.

The definitions of real numbers, their sums, products, etc., are, in fact, such that the ordinary arithmetical manipulations hold for them as for the elementary rationals. If we begin to prove this for particular steps, it soon becomes obvious that such is the case generally, and we shall not attempt to prove up to the hilt for real numbers any property that is reasonably obvious from our experience in dealing with numbers as we understood them before we considered cuts.

6. Upper and lower bounds

We shall use the notation introduced in Chapter II.

THEOREM II. *If (L, R) is a cut denoted by G, then†*

$$\epsilon > 0; \quad \exists \ an \ r \ of \ G \ . \ r' < G+\epsilon;$$

also, $\qquad \exists \ an \ l \ of \ G \ . \ l' > G-\epsilon.$

By the corollary to the definition of a sum,

$$\exists \ an \ l \ of \ G+\epsilon > some \ r \ of \ G. \qquad (1)$$

But $G+\epsilon \geqslant$ each and every l' derived from an E.R. that is an l of the cut $G+\epsilon$.

[NOTE. We cannot say $G+\epsilon \geqslant l$, because $G+\epsilon$ is a real number, while l is an E.R., and we have set up no machinery for comparing a cut of the E.R. with one single E.R.]

Hence

$G+\epsilon \geqslant$ the particular l' derived from the l

that has been found in (1)

$>$ the r' derived from the r found in (1).

† r' is the rational real 'derived from r'.

This proves the first part of the theorem; the second part may be proved in similar fashion.

First fundamental assumption of Chapter III

In the work on convergence that preceded the present discussion of real numbers we built up our theory on the following assumption:

If (α_n) is a sequence of numbers and there is one number $A \geqslant$ every α_n, then there is a least number, U, that is greater than or equal to every α_n.

We are now in a position to prove that this assumption is a *consequence* of our definition of real number.

THEOREM III. *Let $\{a\}$ denote an arbitrary set of real numbers. Let there be a number $A_0 \geqslant$ each and every member of $\{a\}$. Let $\{A\}$ denote the set of all numbers that are greater than or equal to each and every member of $\{a\}$. Then $\{A\}$ possesses a least element U, which is called the UPPER BOUND of $\{a\}$.*

Every rational real number is or is not an A. Define two sets L, R of E.R. thus:—the E.R. c belongs to L if the rational real number derived from it is not an A, and otherwise it belongs to R.

Then there are E.R.'s that belong to L and, since $A_0 \geqslant$ each and every a, there are E.R.'s that belong to R. Also, every E.R. goes either into L or into R, and each and every $l <$ each and every r, so that (L, R) is a cut. Denote this cut by U. By Theorem II,

$$\epsilon > 0; \quad \exists \; r \text{ of } U \text{ such that } U + \epsilon > r',$$

where r' is the rational real derived from r. Hence

$$U + \epsilon > \text{each and every } a. \tag{i}$$

This is true for every positive ϵ, and therefore

$$U \geqslant \text{each and every } a. \tag{ii}$$

N.B. The argument used to derive (ii) from (i) is of frequent occurrence in analysis.

If the argument is not at once clear, consider the following. If (ii) does not hold, then there must be at least one a, say a_1, that exceeds U.
In that case $U + \frac{1}{2}(a_1 - U) < U + (a_1 - U) = a_1,$
i.e. when $\epsilon = \frac{1}{2}(a_1 - U)$, $U + \epsilon <$ a certain a, and (i) is denied.

It follows, then, that U belongs to $\{A\}$.

Moreover, if $U' < U$, $\exists$ an r of $U' <$ an l of U, and so $U' <$ some a (by the way in which L was formed). Hence U is in $\{A\}$ and any number less than U is not.

7. Greatest and least limits

We recall, from Chapter XI, § 2, the formal definition of an 'interval'.

Let $\{a\}$ denote any set of numbers. If x is such that in each and every open interval δ_x containing x there is at least one a other than x itself, then x is called a limit point of $\{a\}$. The number x itself may or may not belong to $\{a\}$—see examples below.

If x is a limit point of $\{a\}$, then each open interval δ_x containing x contains an infinity of a. For, if a given δ_x contained only a finite number of a, then there would be a greatest a that was less than x and a least a that was greater than x; there would be no a other than, possibly, x itself between them. That is, there would be an interval about x with no a, save possibly x, in it. This is contrary to the supposition that x is a limit point of $\{a\}$.

EXAMPLES. If $\{a\}$ consists of all y such that $0 < y < 1$, then every x such that $0 \leqslant x \leqslant 1$ is a limit point of $\{a\}$.

If $\{a\}$ consists of the sequence

$$1, \tfrac{1}{2}, \tfrac{2}{3}, \tfrac{1}{3}, \tfrac{3}{4}, \tfrac{1}{4}, \tfrac{4}{5}, \ldots,$$

then 0 and 1 are the only limit points.

We now consider the greatest limit of a sequence (x_n).

In the first place we suppose that (x_n) is a bounded sequence; i.e. $\exists\ K\ .\ |x_n| < K$ for all n.

Divide the E.R. into L, R thus: the E.R. c goes in R if only a finite number (or none) of the x_n are greater than or equal to c', the rational real derived from c; otherwise c goes in L. Then, as is readily verified, (L, R) is a cut. Denote it by G. We shall show that G is a limit point of (x_n). By Theorem II,

$$\epsilon > 0;\quad \exists\ l, r\ .\ G - \epsilon < l',\quad G + \epsilon > r'.$$

But, by definition,

$l' \leqslant x_n$ for an infinity of values of n,

$r' > x_n$ for all save, possibly, a finite number of values of n.

Hence

$$G - \epsilon < x_n < G + \epsilon \quad \text{for an infinity of values of } n,$$

so that, since ϵ was any positive number whatsoever, G is a limit point of the sequence.

Moreover, *no limit point of (x_n) can exceed G.* For, if $p = G + \alpha$, where $\alpha > 0$, then $\exists$ an r of G such that $r' < G + \frac{1}{2}\alpha$. Hence, there is at most a finite number of values of n for which $x_n \geqslant G + \frac{1}{2}\alpha = p - \frac{1}{2}\alpha$. Hence p is not a limit point.

G is called the greatest limit and is denoted by $\overline{\lim} x_n$.

In the course of the preceding work we have proved the following fact. When $G' > G$, there is at most a finite number of the x_n that exceed G'. Thus, if $G = \overline{\lim} x_n$, then

$$G' > G; \quad \exists \ N \ . \ x_n < G' \quad \text{when } n \geqslant N.$$

This is a most useful property and enters into most applications of the notation $\overline{\lim} x_n$.

THE STATEMENTS $\overline{\lim} x_n = +\infty$, $\overline{\lim} x_n = -\infty$. Suppose now that the sequence (x_n) is not bounded. If, however large we take the E.R. c, $x_n \geqslant c'$ for an infinity of values of n, then we write $\overline{\lim} x_n = +\infty$. If, however large and negative we take c, only a finite number of $x_n \geqslant c'$ (and there is an infinity of x_n altogether), we write $\overline{\lim} x_n = -\infty$.

EXAMPLES.

$$1, 1, 2, \tfrac{1}{2}, 3, \tfrac{1}{3}, \dots; \quad \overline{\lim} x_n = +\infty.$$
$$-1, -2, -3, \dots; \quad \overline{\lim} x_n = -\infty.$$

The least limit

The least limit, written $\underline{\lim} x_n$, is similarly defined.† No limit point can be less than it. Also, if $\underline{\lim} x_n = L$, then

$$L' < L; \quad \exists \ N \ . \ x_n > L' \quad \text{when } n \geqslant N.$$

---

† An alternative definition is effected by 'reflection in the origin' thus: $\underline{\lim} x_n = - \overline{\lim}(-x_n)$. A diagram of points x_n and $-x_n$ will show the reason for this definition.

THE STATEMENT $\lim x_n = x$. As in Chapter II, we say that $\lim x_n = x$ if

$$\epsilon > 0; \quad \exists \ N \ . \ |x-x_n| < \epsilon \quad \text{when } n \geqslant N. \tag{1}$$

It follows, almost directly from the definitions, that $\overline{\lim} x_n$ and $\underline{\lim} x_n$ are then both equal to x. For, if (1) is satisfied, and X is other than x, then only a finite number of the x_n can lie in a closed interval that contains X but excludes x; hence X cannot be a limit point of the x_n.

8. The second fundamental assumption

At the conclusion of § 7 we stated formally the condition that a sequence (x_n) of real numbers should have x as its limit. We now show that

Any irrational real number may be expressed as the limit of a sequence of rational real numbers.

By Theorem II, if G denotes a given real number, then

$$\epsilon > 0; \quad \exists \text{ a rational real } r' \ . \ r' < G+\epsilon.$$

If G is irrational, then this r' cannot be G and we have $r' > G$.

First take $\epsilon = 1$; then there is an r' that satisfies

$$G < r' < G+1.$$

Let $r'-G = \eta$, and let ϵ_1 be any number that is less than both η and $\frac{1}{2}$.

There is then a rational real r_1' that satisfies $G < r_1' < G+\epsilon_1$. Also $r_1' < G+\eta = r'$. Let $r_1'-G = \eta_1$, and let ϵ_2 be any number that is less than both η_1 and $\frac{1}{4}$.

There is then a rational real r_2' that satisfies

$$G < r_2' < G+\epsilon_2.$$

Also $r_2' < G+\eta_1 = r_1'$.

Proceeding in this way, we determine a sequence of rational real numbers $r_1', r_2', ..., r_n', ...$, such that

$$\text{(i)} \quad r_{n+1}' < r_n', \qquad \text{(ii)} \quad r_n' > G, \qquad \text{(iii)} \quad r_n'-G < 2^{-n}.$$

That is to say, we have determined a monotonic decreasing sequence of rational real numbers whose limit is G.

By using the l' of Theorem II instead of the r' we may express G as the limit of a monotonic increasing sequence of rational real numbers.

Thus the assumption of Chapter III, § 3, is proved to be a consequence of the definition of real number.

INDEX

Numbers refer to pages. Attention is called to the entries under 'Definitions' and 'Tests'.